TINY TRAINS

A Guide to Britain's Miniature Railways 2018-2019

EDITOR
John Robinson

Twelfth Edition

RAILWAY LOCATOR MAP

The numbers shown on this map relate to the page numbers for each railway.
Pages 5-6 contain an alphabetical listing of the railways featured in this guide.
Please note that the markers on this map show the approximate location only.

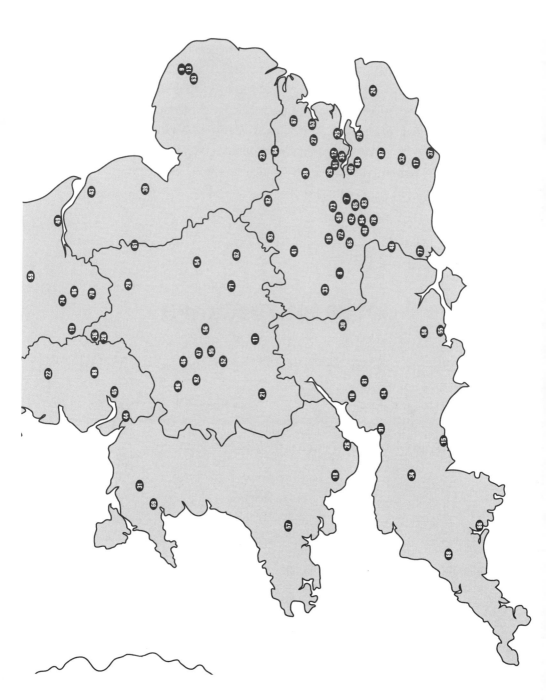

ACKNOWLEDGEMENTS

We were greatly impressed by the friendly and cooperative manner of the staff and helpers of the railways and societies which we selected to appear in this book, and wish to thank them all for the help they have given. In addition we wish to thank Bob Budd (cover design), Michael Robinson (page layouts) and Jonathan James (photographs) for their help.

Although we believe that the information contained in this guide is accurate at the time of going to press, we, and the Railways and Societies itemised, are unable to accept liability for any loss, damage, distress or injury suffered as a result of any inaccuracies. Furthermore, we and the Societies are unable to guarantee operating and opening times which may always be subject to cancellation without notice. For the purposes of this guide we classify railways with gauges of 7¼ inches or less as 'miniature'.

John Robinson

John Robinson

EDITOR

COVER PHOTOGRAPH

The cover photograph was taken on 5th March 2018 at the National Railway Museum and show their tremendously popular 7¼ inch miniature railway which is located in the South Garden of the site.

British Library Cataloguing in Publication Data
A catalogue record for this book is available from the British Library

ISBN-13: 978-1-86223-375-1

Printed in the UK by Short Run Press Limited

CONTENTS

ACTON MINIATURE RAILWAY

Address: London Transport Museum Depot, 118 Gunnersbury Lane, London	**Nº of Steam Locos**: Visiting locos only
	Nº of Other Locos: 6 (plus visiting locos)
Telephone Nº: (01252) 519287	**Nº of Volunteers**: 10 to 20
Year Formed: 2005	**Approx Nº of Visitors P.A.**: 2,000
Location of Line: Museum Depot	**Gauge**: 7¼ inches
Length of Line: 100 yards	**Website**: www.actonminiaturerailway.co.uk

GENERAL INFORMATION

Nearest Mainline Station: South Acton (¾ mile)
Nearest Tube Station: Acton Town (adjacent)
Car Parking: None
Coach Parking: None
Souvenir Shop(s): None
Food & Drinks: None

SPECIAL INFORMATION

The railway is located in the grounds of the London Transport Museum's Depot in Acton and is operated by Friends of the Museum who helped in the line's construction.

OPERATING INFORMATION

Opening Times: 2018 dates: During open weekends only from 11.00am to 5.00pm. Current planned dates are 21st and 22nd April. Please check the Museum's web site for further dates.
Steam Working: Most opening days
Prices: Adults £1.00
Children £1.00
Concessions £1.00
Note: An admission fee to the Museum Depot is payable to access the railway. Under-18s are admitted free of charge (Under-12s must be accompanied by an adult).
Adult Admission £17.50
Concessionary Admission £15.00

Detailed Directions by Car:
As there is no parking available at the Depot, it is recommended that visitors take the Underground to Acton Town Station which is adjacent.

AMNERFIELD MINIATURE RAILWAY

Address: Amners Farm, Burghfield, Berkshire RG30 3UE	**Nº of Steam Locos**: 3
Telephone Nº: (0118) 983-3437	**Nº of Other Locos**: 5
Year Formed: 1995	**Nº of Members**: 13
Location of Line: Amners Farm	**Approx Nº of Visitors P.A.**: 3,000
Length of Line: ¾ mile	**Gauge**: 5 inches and 7¼ inches
	Web site: www.amnersfarm.co.uk

GENERAL INFORMATION

Nearest Mainline Station: Theale (2 miles)
Nearest Bus Station: Reading
Car Parking: Free parking available on site
Coach Parking: None
Souvenir Shop(s): None
Food & Drinks: Available

OPERATING INFORMATION

Opening Times: 2018 dates: 28th & 29th April; 5th, 6th & 7th May; Other operating dates will be announced so please check the web site for further details of these.
Trains run from 2.00pm to 4.30pm
Steam Working: Every operating day.
Prices: Adults £1.50

Detailed Directions by Car:
From All Parts: Exit the M4 at Junction 12 and take the A4 towards Reading. After approximately 2 miles turn right at the traffic lights into Burghfield Road. Continue along this road passing over the motorway then take the first turning on the left into Amners Farm Road. After approximately ½ mile turn right into Amners Farm.

ASHMANHAUGH LIGHT RAILWAY

Address: East View Farm, Stone Lane, Ashmanhaugh, Norwich   NR12 8YW
Telephone Nº: (01603) 404263
Year Formed: 2002
Location of Line: Near Wroxham Barns
Length of Line: 900 yards

Nº of Steam Locos: 4
Nº of Other Locos: 7
Approx Nº of Visitors P.A.: 2,500
Gauge: 7¼ inches
Web site:
www.ashmanhaughlightrailway.co.uk

GENERAL INFORMATION

Nearest Mainline Station: Wroxham & Hoveton (1½ miles)
Nearest Bus Station: Norwich (10 miles)
Car Parking: Available on site
Coach Parking: None
Souvenir Shop(s): None
Food & Drinks: Light refreshments available

SPECIAL INFORMATION

Close to the Bure Valley Line and the Norwich to Sheringham Line, this is a railway operated by enthusiasts set in the beautiful North Norfolk countryside on a delightful 10 acre landscaped site.

OPERATING INFORMATION

Opening Times: 2018 dates: The first Sunday in the month from 6th May to 7th October inclusive, weather permitting.
Trains run from 2.00pm to 5.00pm.
Steam Working: Most operating days.
Prices: Adults £2.00 (Day Rover ticket £4.00)
Children £2.00 (Day Rover ticket £4.00)
Family Day Rover £12.00
(2 adults + 2 children)

Detailed Directions by Car:
From All Parts: Ashmanhaugh is situated just off the A1151 Wroxham to Stalham road. The railway is close to the Wroxham Barns Centre and is signposted from the road on open days.

Ashton Court Estate Miniature Railway

Address: Ashton Court Estate, Long Ashton, North Somerset BS8 3PX	**Nº of Steam Locos**: 3
Telephone Nº: (0117) 946-7110	**Nº of Other Locos**: 4
Year Formed: Opened 1973	**Nº of Members**: 250
Location of Line: Ashton Court Estate	**Approx Nº of Visitors P.A.**: 30,000
Length of Line: Two tracks, each approximately a third of a mile in length	**Gauge**: 3½ inches, 5 inches & 7¼ inches
	Website: www.bristolmodelengineers.co.uk

GENERAL INFORMATION

Nearest Mainline Station: Bristol Temple Meads (Approximately 5 miles)
Nearest Bus Station: Bristol (4 miles)
Car Parking: Parking available on site
Coach Parking: Available by prior arrangement
Souvenir Shop(s): None
Food & Drinks: None

SPECIAL INFORMATION

The Railway is owned and operated by the Bristol Society of Model & Experimental Engineers which was founded in 1909.

OPERATING INFORMATION

Opening Times: 2018 dates: 1st, 2nd, 15th & 29th April; 6th, 7th, 27th & 28th May; 17th & 24th June; 8th & 22nd July; 5th, 26th & 27th August; 9th & 23rd September; 7th & 14th October and Santa Specials on 2nd December (pre-booking required). On operating days, trains run from 12.00pm to 5.00pm.
Steam Working: All operating days.
Prices: 90p per ride per person. Also 5 tickets available for £4.00 and 10 tickets available for £8.00.
Note: Tickets for the very popular Santa Specials are pre-bookable from 6th August.

Detailed Directions by Car:
Exit the M5 at junction 19 and take the A369 towards Bristol. After approximately 6 miles, just past the B3129 traffic lights is Ashton Court Estate. However, there is no right turn from this direction. Instead, take the side road on the left (North Road), turn right into Bridge Road and continue straight across the A369 at the traffic lights into the Clifton Lodge Entrance. Take the first right then the first right again before the golf kiosk car park.

AVONVALE MODEL ENGINEERING SOCIETY

Address: Hillers, Heath Farm, Alcester
Warwickshire   B49 5PD
Phone Nº: (01527) 543350
Year Formed: 2001
Location of Line: Hillers, Dunnington
Length of Line: A third of a mile

Nº of Steam Locos: 16
Nº of Other Locos: 12
Nº of Members: Approximately 40
Approx Nº of Visitors P.A.: 3,000
Gauge: 5 inches and 7¼ inches
Web site: www.avonvale.me.uk

GENERAL INFORMATION

Nearest Mainline Station: Evesham (11 miles)
Nearest Bus Station: Stratford-upon-Avon (13 miles)
Car Parking: Free parking available on site
Coach Parking: None
Souvenir Shop(s): None
Food & Drinks: Available

SPECIAL INFORMATION

The Engines are all privately owned and run as required. The railway is located at Hillers where other attractions include a Café, a Farm Shop and a Display Garden.

OPERATING INFORMATION

Opening Times: 2018 dates: 1st, 14th, 15th, 28th & 29th April; 5th, 6th, 26th & 27th May; 9th, 10th, 23rd & 24th June; 14th, 15th, 28th & 29th July; 11th, 12th, 25th & 26th August; 8th, 9th, 22nd & 23rd September; 6th, 7th, 20th & 21st October. Also a special Halloween event on 30th & 31st October. Trains run from 11.00am to 4.00pm and from 3.00pm to 8.00pm on Halloween event days.
Steam Working: Where possible at least two steam locos run on each operating day.
Prices: 90p per ride per person on normal days
£1.00 per ride on Halloween events
8 tickets cost £6.50

Detailed Directions by Car:
From the North: Take the A435 or A46 to Alcester then follow the B4088 to Dunnington. Once in Dunnington, turn right at the crossroad and Hillers is on the right hand side with the railway visible from the road; From the South: Take the Evesham bypass then follow the B4088 to Dunnington.

BARNARDS MINIATURE RAILWAY

Address: Barnards Farm, Brentwood
Road, West Horndon CM13 3LX
Telephone Nº: (01277) 811262
Year Formed: 2010
Location: Off the A128 between Basildon
& Hornchurch
Length of Line: Almost 1 mile

Nº of Steam Locos: 9
Nº of Other Locos: 6
Approx Nº of Visitors P.A.: 3,000
Gauge: 7¼ inches
Web: www.barnardsminiaturerailway.eu

GENERAL INFORMATION

Nearest Mainline Station:
West Horndon (1½ miles)
Car Parking: Available on site
Coach Parking: Available on site
Souvenir Shop(s): None
Food & Drinks: Available on site

SPECIAL INFORMATION

The Railway is located at Barnards Farm
and runs through 17 hectares of gardens
which range from landscaped walks
through young woodland to the precise
detail of the Japanese garden. A significant
collection of sculpture by artists of many
nationalities is also spread throughout the
gardens.

OPERATING INFO

Opening Times: 2018 dates: 1st, 2nd &
29th April; 13th, 26th, 27th & 31st May;
3rd, 17th & 24th June; 1st, 14th, 15th,
26th & 29th July; 2nd, 9th, 12th, 16th,
23rd, 26th & 30th August; 2nd, 16th &
23rd September; 21st October; 10th &
11th November; 1st, 2nd, 8th & 9th
December (Santa Express).
The gardens are generally open from
11.00am to 4.30pm though they only open
on afternoons on other dates. Please
contact Barnards Farm for details.
Steam Working: Please contact the
railway for further information.
Prices: Adult Return £6.00
        Child Return £5.00
            (Under-3s ride free)
        Child All Day Travel Ticket £8.00
Note: Advance bookings are required for
the Santa Specials which operate during
December. Group visits can often be
arranged by appointment.

Detailed Directions by Car:
From the West: Exit the M25 at Junction 29 and head eastward on the A127. After approximately 6½ miles exit
onto the A128 and follow the road towards Tilbury. Turn right into the Barnard Farm car park shortly after
passing under the railway line; From the East: Follow the A127 westward from Basildon and exit onto the A128
towards Tilbury. Then as above.

BARTON HOUSE RAILWAY

Address: Hartwell Road, The Avenue, Wroxham NR12 8TL
Telephone Nº: (01603) 782008
Year Formed: 1963
Location of Line: Wroxham, Norfolk
Length of Line: 167 yards

Nº of Steam Locos: 4
Nº of Other Locos: 4
Approx Nº of Visitors P.A.: 1,250
Gauge: 3½ inches and 7¼ inches
Web site: www.bartonhouserailway.org.uk
Email: enquiries@bartonhouserailway.org.uk

GENERAL INFO

Nearest Mainline Station: Hoveton and Wroxham (1 mile)
Nearest Bus Station: Wroxham (1 mile)
Car Parking: Limited parking available on site
Coach Parking: None
Souvenir Shop(s): Yes
Food & Drinks: Available

SPECIAL INFO

The original Honing East signalbox was rebuilt at Wroxham to form the basis for the Barton House Railway which is run entirely by volunteers. On open days, a boat service operates from Wroxham Bridge to take passengers to the railway.

OPERATING INFO

Opening Times: The 3rd Sunday each month from April until October and also on Easter Monday. Trains run from 2.30pm to 5.30pm. Also open on the 4th Saturday in September from 7.00pm to 10.00pm.
Steam Working: Most operating days.
Prices: Adults £3.00
Children £1.50
Note: On open days, access to the railway is also available via an electric launch service running from Wroxham Bridge. Prices of this service are shown above.

Detailed Directions by Car:
From the South and West: Take the A1151 from Norwich to Wroxham then follow the road over the railway bridge. Take the 3rd turning on the right into 'The Avenue', first left into Staitheway Road then right into Hartwell Road. The railway is at the end of the road; From the North: Take the A149 to the A1151 to Wroxham, turn left into 'The Avenue', then as above.

BATH & WEST RAILWAY

Address: The Royal Bath and West Showground, Shepton Mallet BA4 6QN	**Nº of Other Locos:** 3
Phone Nº: (01761) 414357 (Chairman)	**Nº of Members:** Approximately 100
Year Formed: 2001	**Annual Membership Fee:** £28.00
Length of Line: ½ mile	**Approx Nº of Visitors P.A.:** 11,000
Nº of Steam Locos: 11	**Gauge:** 5 inches and 7¼ inches
	Web site: www.essmee.org.uk

GENERAL INFORMATION

Nearest Mainline Station: Castle Cary (4 miles)
Nearest Bus Station: Shepton Mallet
Car Parking: Free parking available on site
Coach Parking: Available
Food & Drinks: Available during shows

SPECIAL INFORMATION

The Bath & West Railway is operated by members of the East Somerset Society of Model and Experimental Engineers Ltd.

OPERATING INFORMATION

Opening Times: The railway is situated on The Royal Bath & West Showground, Shepton Mallet. Our operating days, as well as our ability to entertain visitors with their locos, are therefore governed by which particular shows are using the showground. The railway operates on the four days of the Royal Bath & West Show from 30th May to 2nd June 2018. Agreements between the Society and other shows may mean that the railway also operates on other dates during 2018. Please check the Society's web site for further information before visiting. The Society has two open weekends planned, 21st & 22nd April 2018 and 6th & 7th October 2018 when members of the public and other Engineering Societies are invited to visit with their locos and traction engines. Contact details to arrange this can be found on the web site.

Steam Working: All public operating days.
Prices: £2.00 per ride or 8 rides for £10.00
Note: An entrance fee is charged by the show organisers for their events.

Detailed Directions by Car:
From All Parts: The Royal Bath and West Showground is situated approximately 2 miles south of Shepton Mallet just off the A371 road to Castle Cary.

BEER HEIGHTS LIGHT RAILWAY

Address: Pecorama, Beer, East Devon, EX12 3NA
Telephone N°: (01297) 21542
Year Formed: 1975
Location of Line: Beer, East Devon
Length of Line: 1 mile

N° of Steam Locos: 8 at present
N° of Other Locos: 3
Approx N° of Visitors P.A.: 80,000
Gauge: 7¼ inches
Web site: www.pecorama.co.uk
E-mail: pecorama@pecobeer.co.uk

GENERAL INFORMATION

Nearest Mainline Station: Axminster
Nearest Bus Stop: Beer
Car Parking: Available on site
Coach Parking: Available on site
Souvenir Shop(s): Yes
Food & Drinks: Licensed restaurant on site

SPECIAL INFORMATION

In addition to the Railway, Pecorama features a Model Railway Exhibition, childrens activity areas and extensive gardens.

OPERATING INFORMATION

Opening Times: 2018 dates: Daily from 26th March to 31st October.
Steam Working: On every operating day, weather permitting.
Prices: Adult £11.00
Child £9.00 (Under-1s free of charge)
Senior Citizens £10.00 (Over-80s free)
The prices shown above include entry to the Gardens, one ride on the railway and entry to the Model Railway Exhibition.

Detailed Directions by Car:
From All Parts: Take the A3052 to Beer, turn onto the B3174 and follow the Brown Tourist signs for Pecorama.

BEKONSCOT LIGHT RAILWAY

Address: Bekonscot Model Village & Railway, Warwick Road, Beaconsfield, Bucks HP9 2PL
Telephone Nº: (01494) 672919
Year Formed: 2001 (Originally 1929)
Location of Line: Beaconsfield, Bucks.
Length of Line: 400 yards

Nº of Steam Locos: None at present
Nº of Other Locos: 3
Approx Nº of Visitors P.A.: 180,000
Gauge: 7¼ inches
Web site: www.bekonscot.co.uk

GENERAL INFORMATION

Nearest Mainline Station: Beaconsfield (5 minutes walk)
Nearest Bus Station: High Wycombe
Car Parking: Limited spaces adjacent to the site
Coach Parking: Limited spaces adjacent to the site
Souvenir Shop(s): Yes
Food & Drinks: Available

SPECIAL INFORMATION

The Railway is situated in Bekonscot Model Village, a 1½ acre miniature landscape of fields, farms, castles, churches, woods and lakes which also contains a model railway.

OPERATING INFORMATION

Opening Times: 2018 dates: Daily from 10th February to 28th October. Open 10.00am to 5.30pm.
Steam Working: None at present
Prices: Adult £10.00
Child £6.00 (Ages 2–15 years)
Family Ticket £29.00
Concessions £8.00

Note: Prices shown above are for entrance into Bekonscot Model Village which is required to visit the railway. Rides are an additional £1.00 per person. Reduced rates are available for groups of 15 or more.

Detailed Directions by Car:
From All Parts: Exit the M40 at Junction 2 taking the A355 then follow the signs for the "Model Village".

BENTLEY MINIATURE RAILWAY

Address: Bentley Country Park, Halland BN8 5AF	**Nº of Steam Locos**: Members locos only
Telephone Nº: 0845 867-2583	**Nº of Other Locos**: Members locos only
Year Formed: 1985	**Approx Nº of Visitors P.A.**: 50,000 (to the Museum)
Location of Line: 5 miles North of Lewes	**Gauge**: 7¼ inches
Length of Line: 1 mile	**Web site**: www.bentleyrailway.co.uk

GENERAL INFORMATION

Nearest Mainline Station: Uckfield (4 miles)
Nearest Bus Station: Uckfield (4 miles)
Car Parking: Free parking available on site
Coach Parking: Free parking available on site
Souvenir Shop(s): Yes
Food & Drinks: Available

SPECIAL INFORMATION

The railway is owned and operated by members of the Bentley Miniature Railway Ltd. and is located in the grounds of the Bentley Wildfowl & Motor Museum (www.bentley.org.uk) which houses a wide range of other attractions.

OPERATING INFORMATION

Opening Times: Sundays during March, weekends from April to the end of October and daily during August and the East Sussex school holidays. Trains run from 11.30am to 4.00pm (11.00am to 5.00pm during the summer).
Steam Working: Most Sundays.
Prices: Adults £9.00 (Park Entry only)
Children £6.00 (Park Entry only)
Concessions £7.00 (Park Entry only)
Family £28.00 (Park Entry only)
Note: Train rides are an additional £1.00 per person.

E-mail: enquiries@bentleyrailway.co.uk

Detailed Directions by Car:
From All Parts: Bentley Wildfowl & Motor Museum is located just outside of the village of Shortgate by the B2192 road between Halland (which located by at the junction of the B2192 and A22) and Lewes (A26/A27). The Museum is well-signposted locally from the A22 (Uckfield to Eastbourne), A26 (Uckfield to Lewes) and B2192.

BRIDGEND & DISTRICT M.E.S.

Address: Fountain Road, Aberkenfig, Bridgend   CF32 0EH
Telephone Nº: (01656) 740480
Year Formed: 1984
Location of Line: Tondu, near Bridgend
Length of Line: Over 1,200 metres

Nº of Steam Locos: 8
Nº of Other Locos: 10
Nº of Members: Approximately 45
Approx Nº of Visitors P.A.: 4,000
Gauge: 3½ inches, 5 inches & 7¼ inches
Website: www.bridgendminiaturerailway.com

GENERAL INFORMATION

Nearest Mainline Station: Tondu (1 mile)
Nearest Bus Station: Bridgend (2 miles)
Car Parking: Available on site
Coach Parking: Available on site
Food & Drinks: Available

SPECIAL INFORMATION

A 4-inch scale traction engine is available to give rides on most of the Society's open days. A new track extension, almost doubling the length of the line, is now open.

OPERATING INFORMATION

Opening Times: 2018 dates: 7th April; 5th May; 2nd June; 7th, 21st & 28th July; 4th & 18th August; 1st September; 6th & 27th October; 15th & 26th December. Trains run from noon until 4.00pm.
Steam Working: All open days where possible.
Prices: £2.00 per person per ride.
                 6 rides for £10.00
Note: The line is available for birthday party bookings. Please contact the Society for details.

Detailed Directions by Car:
Exit the M4 at Junction 36 and follow the A4063 Northwards. At the first roundabout take the 2nd exit onto the B4281 Park Road. Continue into Fountain Road and turn right (still on Fountain Road). The MES club area is located opposite the entrance to Parc Slip Nature Reserve.

BRIGHOUSE & HALIFAX MODEL ENGINEERS

Address: Ravensprings Park, Cawcliffe Road, Brighouse HD6 2HP	**Nº of Steam Locos:** 50-60
Telephone Nº: (01484) 717140	**Nº of Other Locos:** 2 (traction engines)
Year Formed: 1932	**Nº of Members:** Approximately 75
Location of Line: Ravensprings Park	**Approx Nº of Visitors P.A.:** 4,500
Length of Line: 650 feet (5 inch gauge) and 1,200 feet (7¼ inch gauge)	**Gauge:** 2½ inches, 3½ inches, 5 inches and 7¼ inches
	Web site: www.bhme.co.uk

GENERAL INFORMATION

Nearest Mainline Station: Brighouse (1½ miles)
Nearest Bus Station: Brighouse (1 mile)
Car Parking: Available on site
Coach Parking: Available by prior arrangement
Food & Drinks: Available on open days

OPERATING INFORMATION

Opening Times: 2018 dates: 8th April; 13th May; 10th & 24th June; 8th July; 12th August; 9th September; 14th October.
Trains run from 1.30pm to 5.00pm.
Steam Working: All operating days.
Prices: Adults £3.00 (unlimited rides)
       Children £2.00 (unlimited rides)
       Concessions £2.00 (unlimited rides)

Detailed Directions by Car:
Ravensprings Park lies in the Northern part of Brighouse. From the South: Take the A641 Bradford Road northwards and turn left just after the Thaal Indian Restaurant into Cross Street for Smith Carr Lane. Turn right into Bracken Road then left into Cawcliffe Road for the Park; From the North: Travel into Brighouse on the A641 and turn right just before the Thaal Indian Restaurant into Cross Street. Then as above.

BROOKSIDE MINIATURE RAILWAY

Address: London Road North (A523), Poynton, Cheshire SK12 1BY **Telephone N°:** (01625) 872919 **Year Formed:** 1989 **Location:** Brookside Garden Centre **Length of Line:** Approximately ½ mile	**N° of Steam Locos:** 5 **N° of Other Locos:** 3 **Approx N° of Visitors P.A.:** 70,000 **Gauge:** 7¼ inches **Web:** www.brooksideminiaturerailway.co.uk

GENERAL INFORMATION

Nearest Mainline Station: Poynton and Hazel Grove (both 1 mile)
Nearest Bus Station: Stockport (5 miles).
Car Parking: 300 spaces available on site
Coach Parking: 2 spaces available
Souvenir Shop(s): Yes
Food & Drinks: Yes

SPECIAL INFORMATION

The Railway runs through the grounds of the Brookside Garden Centre. There is also an extensive collection of Railwayana on display.

OPERATING INFORMATION

Opening Times: The Railway is open on weekends and Bank Holidays plus Wednesdays from April to September. Open every day in July and August as well as during School holidays. Trains usually run from 10.45am to 4.00pm but only until 3.30pm from November to February.
Steam Working: Weekends and Bank Holidays only
Prices: Adult £2.00 per ride (10 ride tickets £15.00)
Child £2.00 per ride (10 ride tickets £15.00)
Under-2s ride for free
Note: The above prices may be subject to change so please check the web site for further details.

Detailed Directions by Car:
From the North: Exit the M60 at Junction 1 in Stockport and take the A6 (signposted Buxton). Upon reaching Hazel Grove, take the A523 to Poynton. Follow the brown tourist signs for the Railway; From the West: Exit the M56 at Junction 6 signposted Wilmslow and continue to Poynton. Follow the brown signs for the Railway; From the South: Exit the M6 at Junction 18 for Holmes Chapel. Follow the signs to Wilmslow, then as from the West; From the East: Follow the A6 to Hazel Grove, then as from the North.

BROOMY HILL RAILWAY

Address: Broomy Hill, Hereford	**Nº of Steam Locos**: 4+
Telephone Nº: (01989) 762119	**Nº of Other Locos**: 1+
Year Formed: 1962	**Nº of Members**: Approximately 80
Location of Line: Adjacent to the	**Approx Nº of Visitors P.A.**: Not known
Waterworks Museum, Hereford	**Gauge**: 7¼ inches, 5 inches, 3½ inches
Length of Line: 1 kilometre	**Web site**: www.hsme.co.uk

GENERAL INFORMATION

Nearest Mainline Station: Hereford (1½ miles)
Nearest Bus Station: Hereford (1½ miles)
Car Parking: Free parking available on site
Coach Parking: Available by prior arrangement
Souvenir Shop(s): Yes
Food & Drinks: Available

SPECIAL INFORMATION

The Broomy Hill Railway is operated by the
Hereford Society of Model Engineers and has two
separate tracks which run along the bank of the
River Wye. Members run their own locomotives so
the number and variety in operation may vary from
day to day. Entry to the site is free of charge and
picnic areas are available.

OPERATING INFORMATION

Opening Times: 2018 dates: 29th April;
13th, 27th & 28th May; 10th & 24th June;
8th & 29th July; 12th, 26th & 27th August;
9th & 30th September; 14th & 27th October.
Trains run from 12.00pm to 4.30pm (2.00pm to
6.00pm for the Halloween trains on 27th October).
Steam Working: All operating days.
Prices: Adults   £1.50 per ride
              Children   £1.50 per ride
Note: Four rides can be bought for £5.00 and
children's parties can be arranged. Also, the site is
prone to flooding so open days may sometimes be
cancelled following heavy rainfall.

Detailed Directions by Car:
From the centre of Hereford, take the A49 Ross-on-Wye Road, turning right into Barton Road. After approximately
400 metres, turn left into Broomy Hill Road, proceed for around 600 metres before turning left following signs
for the Waterworks Museum. The railway is on the right just after the museum which is signposted with Brown
Tourist Information Signs.

BURNLEY & PENDLE MINIATURE RAILWAY (THOMPSON PARK RAILWAY)

Contact Telephone Nº: 07957 714148
Year Formed: 1990
Location: Thompson Park,
Ormerod Road, Burnley   BB11 2RU
Length of Line: 1 kilometre
Gauge: 7¼ inches
Web site: www.bpmrs.org.uk

Nº of Steam Locos: 3 (Member's locos)
Nº of Other Locos: 8
Nº of Members: 36
Annual Membership Fee: £10.00
Approx Nº of Visitors P.A.: 19,000
Facebook Page: 'Thompson Park Railway'

GENERAL INFORMATION

Nearest Mainline Station: Burnley Central (1 mile)
Nearest Bus Station: Burnley (1 mile)
Car Parking: A Pay and Display car park is planned to be in place during 2018.
Coach Parking: Not available
Food & Drinks: Available from a kiosk in the Park

OPERATING INFORMATION

Opening Times: Weekends and Bank Holidays from March until the end of October. Also on Wednesdays during the School Holidays. Special events are held on the last Sunday in June, July and August. Please check the facebook page for details. Trains run between 12.00pm and 4.00pm.
Steam Working: Most operating days.
Prices: £1.00 per person per ride
Note: Dogs are not allowed in Thompson Park!

Detailed Directions by Car:
The Railway runs through Thompson Park in Burnley. The main entrance to this is in Ormerod Road which is just a short distance from the town centre and also near to Turf Moor, the home of Burnley FC.

CAMBRIDGE & DISTRICT MODEL ENGINEERING SOCIETY

Address: Fulbrooke Road, Cambridge, CB3 9EE	**Nº of Steam Locos**: 12
Telephone Nº: none	**Nº of Other Locos**: 4
Year Formed: 1938	**Nº of Members**: 90
Location of Line: Newnham, Cambridge	**Approx Nº of Visitors P.A.**: 3,500
Length of Line: ¾ mile	**Gauge**: 3½ inches, 5 inches and 7¼ inches
	Web site: www.cambridgemes.co.uk

GENERAL INFORMATION

Nearest Mainline Station: Cambridge (2 miles)
Nearest Bus Station: Drummer Street (1 mile)
Car Parking: Available on site (no street parking)
Coach Parking: None
Souvenir Shop(s): None
Food & Drinks: Cafe open on operating days

SPECIAL INFORMATION

The Cambridge & District MES was formed in 1938 and the track and clubhouse in Fulbrooke Road was constructed on a 2 acre site during 1959.

OPERATING INFORMATION

Opening Times: 2018 dates: 13th May, 10th June, 8th July, 12th August, 9th September and 14th October. Open from 12.30pm to 5.30pm.
Steam Working: Every operating day.
Prices: Adults £1.50 per ride (4 rides for £5.00)
Concessions £1.50 per ride (4 rides for £5)
Children £1.50 per ride (4 rides for £5.00)
Note: Under-5s must be accompanied by an adult and Under-3s ride free of charge.

Detailed Directions by Car:
The Railway is located in the south-western part of Cambridge in the suburb of Newnham, just behind the ground of Cambridge Rugby Club. Access to the site is via Fulbrooke Road and, on operating days, the railway is signposted from the A603 (Barton Road).

CANTERBURY & DISTRICT M.E.S.

Address: Brett Quarry, Fordwich,
Near Canterbury, Kent
Phone Nº: 0774 101-2004 (Vice chairman)
Year Formed: 1972
Location of Line: Brett Quarry, Fordwich
Length of Line: 750 feet

Nº of Steam Locos: (As provided by the
Nº of Other Locos: MES members)
Nº of Members: Approximately 60
Gauge: 3½ inches and 5 inches
Web site: www.cdmes.org

GENERAL INFORMATION

Nearest Mainline Station: Sturry (½ mile)
Nearest Bus Station: Canterbury (3 miles)
Car Parking: None on site
Coach Parking: None
Food & Drinks: None

SPECIAL INFORMATION

The Canterbury & District Model Engineering
Society runs a track on land kindly loaned by Bretts
of Fordwich which is open to the public on some
Sunday afternoons throughout the year, weather
permitting.

OPERATING INFORMATION

Opening Times: 2018 dates: 8th April; 13th May;
10th June; 8th July; 9th September; 14th October.
Trains run from 2.00pm onwards, weather
permitting.
Steam Working: Most operating days depending on
which locos have been provided by the MES
members.
Prices: Free rides although donations are accepted
for the upkeep of the track.

Detailed Directions by Car:
From the A28 at Sturry turn into Fordwich Road then left into Marlowe Meadows (look for the Brett sign). Drive
towards the large green gates then walk through following the access road. Please note that the railway is on
private land and access to the public is limited so please do not drive down this road as there is no parking on-site.

CANVEY MINIATURE RAILWAY

Address: Waterside Farm Sports Centre, Somnes Avenue, Canvey Island, Essex, SS8 9RA
Telephone Nº: (01268) 681679
Year Formed: 1976
Location of Line: Canvey Island
Length of Line: Two lines, one of 1,440 feet and one of 4,400 feet (7¼ inch line)

Nº of Steam Locos: Variable
Nº of Other Locos: Variable
Nº of Members: Approximately 80
Approx Nº of Visitors P.A.: 6,000
Gauge: 3½ inches, 5 inches & 7¼ inches
Web site: www.cramec.org

GENERAL INFORMATION

Nearest Mainline Station: Benfleet (1 mile)
Nearest Bus Station: Bus stop just outside
Car Parking: Available on site
Coach Parking: Available on site
Food & Drinks: None

SPECIAL INFORMATION

The railway is operated by members of the Canvey Railway and Model Engineering Club.

OPERATING INFORMATION

Opening Times: 2018 dates: Every Sunday from the 1st April until 14th October. Also open for Santa Specials on dates on 2nd & 9th December.
Please contact the railway for further information. Trains run from 10.30am to 3.45pm.
Steam Working: When available on operating days.
Prices: £1.00 per ride.
Also £5.00 for 6 rides or £9.00 for 12 rides.
Note: Higher prices apply for Santa Specials.

Detailed Directions by Car:
All road routes to Canvey Island meet at the Waterside Farm roundabout. The railway lines are located in the grounds of the Sports Complex/Leisure Centre. Turn right at the traffic lights into the centre and the car park is on the left with the railway on the right.

CARDIFF MODEL ENGINEERING SOCIETY

Address: King George V Drive East, Heath Park, Cardiff CF14 4AW
Telephone Nº: (029) 2025-5000
Year Formed: 1948
Location of Line: Heath Park, Cardiff
Length of Line: 2 tracks of 1,000 feet each plus a tram track of 700 feet

Nº of Steam Locos: 8 (plus many
Nº of Other Locos: 4   members locos)
Nº of Members: Approximately 190
Approx Nº of Visitors P.A.: 12,000
Gauge: 3½ inches, 5 inches & 7¼ inches
Web site: www.cardiffmes.com

GENERAL INFORMATION

Nearest Mainline Station: Heath Low Level (½ mile)
Nearest Bus Stop: Allensbank Road
Car Parking: Available on site and also nearby
Coach Parking: None
Food & Drinks: Available

SPECIAL INFORMATION

The Cardiff Model Engineering society moved to Heath Park in 1987. The site, which includes two railway tracks and a unique electric tramway, an '00' gauge model railway, a garden railway catering for 32mm & 45mm gauges and extensive refreshment facilities, has been developed by the members for the benefit of visitors.

OPERATING INFORMATION

Opening Times: 2018 public dates: 12th & 29th April; 27th & 28th May; 24th June; 22nd July; 26th & 27th August; 23rd September; 14th October. Also a ticket-only Santa Special service on 9th December (Note: These Santa Special tickets are only on sale on 23rd September and cost £4.00 for adults and £10.00 for children).
Trains run from 1.00pm to 5.00pm.
Steam Working: All operating days.
Prices: £1.80 entry per person then £1.80 per ride. Children aged 3 and under are admitted and ride free of charge.

Detailed Directions by Car:
Exit the M4 at Junction 32 and travel towards Cardiff. Turn left at the 3rd set of traffic lights (by the Tesco garage) and continue through 3 sets of traffic lights to the T-junction lights. Turn left here then immediately right then take the 1st left onto King George V Drive. Turn left at the roundabout and take the lane 400 yards on the right.

CHELMSFORD SOCIETY MODEL ENGINEERS

Address: Meteor Way (off Waterhouse Lane), Chelmsford, Essex CM1 2RL
Telephone Nº: None
Year Formed: 1935
Location of Line: Chelmsford
Length of Line: Two tracks, each approximately 1,000 feet long
Web site: www.chelmsfordsocietyofmodelengineers.org.uk

Nº of Steam Locos: 40+ (owned by
Nº of Other Locos: 20+   members)
Nº of Members: Approximately 100
Approx Nº of Visitors P.A.: 1,500
Gauge: 3½ inches, 5 inches & 7¼ inches

GENERAL INFORMATION

Nearest Mainline Station: Chelmsford (½ mile)
Nearest Bus Station: Chelmsford (½ mile)
Car Parking: Available adjacent to the railway (currently free of charge at weekends)
Food & Drinks: Light refreshments available

SPECIAL INFORMATION

The Chelmsford Society of Model Engineers promotes the safe construction and operation of passenger-carrying steam, electric and diesel hauled trains, traction engines and other scale models.

OPERATING INFORMATION

Opening Times: 2018 dates: Every Sunday from 7th April to 6th October inclusive. Trains usually run from 2.00pm to 4.30pm on these dates.
A number of Special Events are held during the year. Please check the Society's web site for further details.
Steam Working: Most operating days.
Prices: £5.00 for 6 rides.

Detailed Directions by Car:
From London: Follow the A12 then take the A1016 towards Chelmsford town centre. Continue past the A414 junctions into Westway then into Waterhouse Lane. Meteor Way is on the right after the fourth set of traffic lights, just before the river. Park and then proceed past the five bar gate to the club entrance on the right; From Southend: Follow the A130 to the A12 junction then cross onto the A1114. After 1¼ miles join the A414 towards Chelmsford. Follow the A414 around Chelmsford to the junction with the A1016 at Widford. Take the 2nd exit into Westway then as from London; From Colchester: Follow the A12 and exit at the A414 junction towards Chelmsford. Follow the A414 to the A1016, then as from Southend.

CHESTERFIELD & DISTRICT M.E.S.

Address: The Clubhouse, Hady Hill, Bolsover Road, Chesterfield S41 0EE
Telephone Nº: None
Year Formed: 1932
Location of Line: In the grounds of St. Peter & St. Paul School, Chesterfield
Length of Line: Two lines – one of 1,100 feet and one of 2,500 feet

Nº of Steam Locos: 1 + members engines
Nº of Other Locos: 3 + members engines
Nº of Members: Approximately 230
Approx Nº of Visitors P.A.: 5,000
Gauge: 2½ inches, 3½ inches, 5 inches and 7¼ inches
Web site: www.cdmes.co.uk

GENERAL INFORMATION

Nearest Mainline Station: Chesterfield (1½ miles)
Nearest Bus Station: Chesterfield (1 mile)
Car Parking: Available on site
Coach Parking: Available by prior arrangement
Food & Drinks: Available

SPECIAL INFORMATION

The Society's aims are to bring together persons from all walks of life who share a common interest in miniature engineering in all its forms.
The excellent facilities at Hady include tracks for locomotives and there are also areas for traction engines to show their paces. As the land is undulating, both the ground level and raised tracks make challenging driving for all locomotives.

OPERATING INFORMATION

Opening Times: 2018 dates: 22nd April, 19th & 20th May, 24th June, 2nd September, 14th October and Fridays from 27th July to 24th August. Santa Specials operate on 9th and 16th December. Trains run from 12.00pm to 4.00pm.
Please contact the railway for further details.
Steam Working: All operational days.
Prices: Admission is free. Rides are £1.50 per person per ride.

Detailed Directions by Car:
The Society is located on the top of Hady Hill, two-thirds of a mile from the town on Bolsover Road, A632. Driving out of Chesterfield, as you get to the top of the steep hill, turn left off the main road into the grounds of St. Peter & St. Paul School. Follow the drive around to the left and then take the first right. The site is at the end of the drive, after about 250 yards.

CHINGFORD & DISTRICT M.E.C.

Address: Ridgeway Park, Peel Close,
Old Church Road, Chingford   E4 6XU
Telephone Nº: None
Year Formed: 1945
Location: Ridgeway Park, Chingford
Length of Lines: 1,000 feet (5 inch track)
and 3,000 feet (7¼ inch track)
Web site: www.chingford-model-engineering.com

Nº of Steam Locos: 11 (owned by Club)
Nº of Other Locos: Many
Nº of Members: 100+
Annual Membership Fee: £25.00 Adult
Approx Nº of Visitors P.A.: 17,000
Gauge: 3½ inches, 5 inches & 7¼ inches

GENERAL INFORMATION

Nearest Mainline Station: Chingford (1½ miles)
Nearest Underground Station: Walthamstow
Central (5 miles)
Car Parking: Limited spaces within the Park
Coach Parking: None
Food & Drinks: None

SPECIAL INFORMATION

The Chingford & District Model Engineering Club
seeks to promote all forms of model engineering
and model making. It's members come from all
walks of life, and do not necessarily have an
engineering background.

OPERATING INFORMATION

Opening Times: Sundays and Bank Holidays from
April to September inclusive. Train rides usually
start at 2.00pm.
Steam Working: Practically every operating day.
Prices: £1.00 per person per ride on the raised track
£1.50 per person per ride on the ground track

Detailed Directions by Car:
Ridgeway Park is situated off the A112 Old Church Road in Chingford. Turn into Peel Close and the Park entrance
is on the left after 50 yards at the mini-roundabout. A small car park is situated in Ridgeway Park. The railway
itself is located about 150 yards down the main path on the right.

COATE WATER PARK MINIATURE RAILWAY

Address: Coate Water Country Park, Swindon, Wiltshire   SN3 6AA
Telephone Nº: (01666) 577596 (Secretary)
Year Formed: 1964
Location of Line: Coate Water Country Park, Swindon
Length of Line: ¾ mile (1,250 metres)

Nº of Steam/Other Locos: A number of different locos are supplied for use by members of the Society
Nº of Members: Approximately 70
Approx Nº of Visitors P.A.: 26,000
Gauge: 5 inches and 7¼ inches
Web site: www.nwmes.info

GENERAL INFORMATION

Nearest Mainline Station: Swindon (2 miles)
Nearest Bus Station: Swindon (2 miles)
Car Parking: Available in the Park
Coach Parking: None
Food & Drinks: Available in the Park

SPECIAL INFORMATION

The Coate Water Park Miniature Railway is operated by the North Wilts Model Engineering Society.

OPERATING INFORMATION

Opening Times: Sundays, Bank Holiday Mondays and some Saturdays. Open from 11.00am with trains running until approximately 5.00pm in the summer months, weather permitting.
Please contact the railway for further information.
Steam Working: Depends which locos have been provided for use on the day by the individual members.
Prices: £2.00 per person per ride.

Detailed Directions by Car:
From Junction 15 of the M4, take the A419 North. Take the first exit left onto the A4259 towards Swindon and follow the dual-carriageway past the Great Western Hospital then turn left at the roundabout for Coate Water Park and follow the road to the main car park. From the car park walk round to the left for the railway.

CONWY VALLEY RAILWAY MUSEUM

Address: Old Goods Yard, Betws-y-Coed, Conwy, North Wales LL24 0AL	**N⁰ of Steam Locos**: 2
Telephone N⁰: (01690) 710568	**N⁰ of Other Locos**: 2
Year Formed: 1983	**Approx N⁰ of Visitors P.A.**: 50,000
Location of Line: Betws-y-Coed	**Gauge**: 7¼ inches and 15 inches
Length of Line: One and an eighth miles	**Web**: www.conwyrailwaymuseum.co.uk

GENERAL INFORMATION

Nearest Mainline Station: Betws-y-Coed (20 yards)
Nearest Bus Station: 40 yards
Car Parking: Car park at site
Coach Parking: Car park at site
Souvenir Shop(s): Yes
Food & Drinks: Yes – Buffet Coach Cafe

SPECIAL INFORMATION

The Museum houses the unique 3D dioramas by the late Jack Nelson. Also the ¼ size steam loco 'Britannia'. The railway has rebuilt two Denver and Rio Grande C16 locomotives for use on the line. It also operates an Isle of Man loco – "Douglas".

OPERATING INFORMATION

Opening Times: Daily from 10.00am to 5.00pm.
Trains Working: Daily from 10.15am
Prices: Adult – £1.50 museum entry
      Child/Senior Citizen – £1.00 museum entry
      Family tickets – £4.00 museum entry
      Train Rides £2.00 per person

Note: Tram rides are usually available on a 15 inch gauge single-deck tram using a specially-built ½ mile track running alongside the mainline. However, due to flooding on Boxing Day, this may be out of operation until later in 2018.
'Toby', a self-drive electric tram for children runs on a 7¼ inch gauge track by the Coach Cafe.

Detailed Directions by Car:
From Midlands & South: Take M54/M6 onto the A5 and into Betws-y-Coed; From Other Parts: Take the A55 coast road then the A470 to Betws-y-Coed. The museum is located by the Mainline Station directly off the A5.

CROWBOROUGH MINIATURE RAILWAY

Address: Goldsmiths Leisure Centre, Eridge Road, Crowborough TN6 2TN **Telephone Nº**: (01892) 852741 **Year Formed**: 1990 **Location of Line**: Crowborough **Length of Line**: 1,000 feet **Web site**: www.crowboroughminiaturerailway.com	**Nº of Steam Locos**: Members locos only **Nº of Other Locos**: 1 **Nº of Members**: 30 **Approx Nº of Visitors P.A.**: 1,000 **Gauge**: 3½ inches, 5 inches & 7¼ inches

GENERAL INFORMATION

Nearest Mainline Station: Crowborough (1½ miles)
Nearest Bus Station: Tunbridge Wells (7 miles)
Car Parking: Available on site
Coach Parking: Available on site
Food & Drinks: Available at the Leisure Centre

SPECIAL INFORMATION

The Crowborough Locomotive Society was formed to build, maintain, and run a miniature railway at the Goldsmiths Leisure Centre in Crowborough. The society runs live steam working locomotives to give both young and old alike a railway journey in miniature!

OPERATING INFORMATION

Opening Times: Saturday afternoons and selected Sundays from Easter until early November. Trains run from 2.00pm to 5.00pm.
Steam Working: Most operational days, depending on which members' locos are running.
Prices: £1.00 for one circuit of the extended track
          £2.50 for a Day Rover ticket
Note: Birthday parties can be held at the railway by prior arrangement.

Detailed Directions by Car:
Goldsmiths Leisure Centre is situated in the north of Crowborough just off the A26 (Eridge Road) which is the main Tunbridge Wells to Uckfield through road.

CUTTESLOWE PARK MINIATURE RAILWAY

Address: Cutteslowe Park, Harbord Road, Oxford   OX2 8ES
(SatNav OX2 8LH – House Number 41!)
Phone Nº: 07900 972380 (Secretary)
Year Formed: 1955
Location: Cutteslowe Park, Oxford
Length of Line: Two lines – 390 yard raised line and 250 yard ground level line

Nº of Steam Locos: 40
Nº of Other Locos: 10
Nº of Members: Approximately 110
Approx Nº of Visitors P.A.: 10,000
Gauge: 3½ inches, 5 inches & 7¼ inches
Web site: www.cosme.org.uk

GENERAL INFORMATION

Nearest Mainline Station: Oxford (3¼ miles)
Nearest Bus Station: Oxford (3 miles)
Car Parking: Available on site
Coach Parking: Available by prior arrangement
Food & Drinks: Refreshments are available in Cutteslowe Park

SPECIAL INFORMATION

The Cutteslowe Park Miniature Railway is operated by the City of Oxford Society of Model Engineers.

OPERATING INFORMATION

Opening Times: 2018 dates: Every 1st and 3rd Sunday from 6th May to 21st October inclusive. Trains run from 1.30pm to 5.00pm (4.30pm in October).
Steam Working: Up to 5 steam locomotives run on every operating day.
Prices: Adults £1.00   Children £1.00
             10 rides are available for £8.00

Detailed Directions by Car:
From outside of Oxford join the ringroad and head to the North of the city. At the roundabout at the junction of the A40 ringroad and the A4165 Banbury Road, head North signposted for Kidlington. Take the third turn on the right into Harbord Road which leads directly into the Park. Follow the signs from the car park for the Railway.

DEVON RAILWAY CENTRE

Address: Bickleigh, Tiverton, Devon, EX16 8RG
Telephone Nº: (01884) 855671
Year Formed: 1997
Location of Line: Bickleigh, Devon
Length of Line: ½ mile (2 foot and 7¼ inch gauges); 200 yards (Standard gauge)

Nº of Steam Locos: 1
Nº of Other Locos: 12
Approx Nº of Visitors P.A.: Not recorded
Gauge: 2 feet, 7¼ inches and Standard
Web site: www.devonrailwaycentre.co.uk
E-mail: devonrailway@btinternet.com

GENERAL INFORMATION

Nearest Mainline Station: Exeter
Nearest Bus Station: Tiverton (Route 55)
Car Parking: Available on site
Coach Parking: Available on site
Souvenir Shop(s): Yes
Food & Drinks: Yes

SPECIAL INFORMATION

Devon Railway Centre has passenger carrying lines and also features a large model railway exhibition with 15 working layouts. A delightful Edwardian model village built to a 1:12 scale has recently been extended with a model funfair added and a new museum coach opened recently.

OPERATING INFORMATION

Opening Times: 2018 dates: Daily from 30th March to 15th April, 23rd May to 9th September and 20th to 28th October. Closed on Mondays in June. Open Wednesday to Sunday inclusive from 2nd to 20th May and 12th to 30th September. Also open during weekends in October. Open from 10.30am until 5.00pm on all operating days.
Steam Working: Miniature trains are diesel-hauled, but narrow gauge trains may be steam or diesel hauled. Please phone for further details.
Prices: Adult £8.40   Child £7.40
       Senior Citizen £7.60   Family £29.40
Admission includes unlimited train rides and access to the model village, model railways and museum.

Detailed Directions by Car:
From All Parts: Devon Railway Centre is situated adjacent to the famous Bickleigh Bridge, just off the A396 Exeter to Tiverton road (3 miles from Tiverton and 8 miles from Exeter).

DOCKLAND & EAST LONDON M.E.S. (BELHUS WOODS RAILWAY)

Address: Belhus Woods Country Park, Romford Road, Aveley RM15 4XJ
Phone N°: (01708) 222658 (Secretary)
Year Formed: 1985
Location: Belhus Woods Country park
Length of Line: 500 feet

N° of Steam Locos: 1
N° of Other Locos: 3
Approx N° of Visitors P.A.: 850
Gauge: 5 inches and 7¼ inches
Website: www.belhus-woods-railway.co.uk

GENERAL INFORMATION

Nearest Mainline Station:
Upminster (4 miles)
Nearest Bus Station:
Grays (5 miles)
Car Parking:
Pay & Display parking available on site
Coach Parking: Small coaches only
Souvenir Shop(s):
Yes – Country Park shop
Food & Drinks:
Light refreshments available

SPECIAL INFORMATION

The Railway is located in Belhus Woods, a beautiful Country Park which has picnic areas adjacent to the track and woodland walks through areas full of waterfowl.

OPERATING INFORMATION

Opening Times: 2018 dates: The 1st Sunday of the month from May to October inclusive. Trains run from 1.00pm to 4.30pm on these dates. Also open for a special Funday on 25th August, 11.00am to 4.00pm.
Steam Working: Weather permitting, both Steam-hauled and Electric services should run on every operating day.
Prices: 60p per person per ride.

Detailed Directions by Car:
Exit the M25 at Junction 29 and follow the A127 towards Romford. After 1 mile turn off at the Hall Lane exit by the flyover and head South towards Upminster. Continue down Hall Lane following through into Station Road then Corbets Tey Road. Upon reaching the T-junction turn right into Harwood Hall Lane then left at the mini-roundabout into Aveley Road. Belhus Woods Country Park is on the left after about 1¼ miles.

DRAGON MINIATURE RAILWAY

Address: Marple Garden Centre, Dooley Lane, Marple, Stockport SK6 7HE	**N⁰ of Steam Locos**: 5
Telephone N⁰: 07748 581160	**N⁰ of Other Locos**: 5
Year Formed: 1999	**Approx N⁰ of Visitors P.A.**: 30,000
Location of Line: Marple Garden Centre	**Gauge**: 7¼ inches
Length of Line: ½ mile	**Web site**: www.freewebs.com/dragonrailway/

GENERAL INFORMATION

Nearest Mainline Station: Romley (1 mile)
Nearest Bus Station: Stockport (2½ miles)
Car Parking: Available on site
Coach Parking: Available
Souvenir Shop(s): Yes
Food & Drinks: Available

SPECIAL INFORMATION

Dragon Miniature Railway is one of the few Garden Centre-based railways which operates steam on most open days.

OPERATING INFORMATION

Opening Times: Weekends and Bank Holidays and also daily during local school holidays throughout the year. Trains run from 11.00am to 4.30pm, weather permitting.
Steam Working: Most operating days.
Prices: £1.00 per ride (Under-2s free of charge)
            Ten-ride tickets are available for £8.00

Detailed Directions by Car:
From All Parts: Exit the M60 at Junction 25, pass through Bredbury and follow signs for Marple along the A627. Cross over the River Goyt and Marple Garden Centre is on the left.

EASTBOURNE MINIATURE STEAM RAILWAY

Address: Lottbridge Drove, Eastbourne, East Sussex BN23 6QJ
Telephone Nº: (01323) 520229
Year Formed: 1992
Location of Line: Eastbourne
Length of Line: 1 mile

Nº of Steam Locos: 8
Nº of Other Locos: 3
Approx Nº of Visitors P.A.: Not known
Gauge: 7¼ inches
Web site: www.emsr.co.uk

GENERAL INFORMATION

Nearest Mainline Station: Eastbourne (2 miles)
Nearest Bus Station: Eastbourne (2 miles)
Car Parking: Free parking on site
Coach Parking: Free parking on site
Souvenir Shop(s): Yes
Food & Drinks: Yes

SPECIAL INFORMATION

The Railway site also has many other attractions including model railways, an adventure playground, maze, nature walk, picnic area and a Cafe.

OPERATING INFORMATION

Opening Times: 2018 dates: Daily from 24th March until 28th October. Trains run from 10.00am to 5.00pm during these days.
Steam Working: Weekends, Bank Holidays and during School Holidays. Diesel at other times.
Prices: Adult £5.50
         Child £5.00 (Under-3s ride free)
         Family Tickets £19.00
                    (2 adults + 2 children)

Detailed Directions by Car:
From All Parts: Take the A22 new road to Eastbourne then follow the Brown tourist signs for the 'Mini Railway'.

EAST HERTS MINIATURE RAILWAY

Address: Van Hage Garden Centre, Great Amwell, near Ware SG12 9RP	**Nº of Steam Locos**: 3
Telephone Nº: (020) 8292-2997	**Nº of Other Locos**: 3
Year Formed: 1978	**Nº of Members**: Approximately 40
Location: Van Hage Garden Centre	**Annual Membership Fee**: £16.00
Length of Line: 500 metres	**Approx Nº of Visitors P.A.**: 40,000
	Gauge: 7¼ inches
	Web site: www.ehmr.org.uk

GENERAL INFORMATION

Nearest Mainline Station: Ware (1½ miles)
Nearest Bus Station: Bus stop outside the Centre
Car Parking: Available on site
Coach Parking: Available
Food & Drinks: Available in the Garden Centre

SPECIAL INFORMATION

The Railway operates a line at the Van Hage Garden Centre in Great Amwell. The railway is run by volunteers and any profits are donated to the local special needs school and other local charities.

OPERATING INFORMATION

Opening Times: Weekends and Bank Holidays throughout the year. Also open Tuesdays and Thursdays during the school holidays. Usually open from 11.00am to 5.00pm but from 10.30am to 4.30pm on Sundays.
Steam Working: Most operating days.
Prices: £1.00 per person per ride. Under-2s travel free of charge and Under-8s must be accompanied by an older, fare-paying passenger.

Detailed Directions by Car:
From the South: Take the A10 towards Cambridge and exit at the first Ware junction signposted for A414. Take the 2nd exit at the roundabout onto the A1170 towards Ware and Van Hage Garden Centre is on the left after 600 metres; From the East: Take the A414 from Harlow and turn off onto the A1170 for Ware. Then as above.

EVERGREENS MINIATURE RAILWAY

Address: Dawn Bank, Keal Cotes, Lincolnshire   PE23 4AE
Telephone N°: (01754) 830574 or (01205) 480703
Year Formed: 2002
Location: Keal Coates, just off the A16
Web site: www.evergreensminiaturerailway.org
E-mail: evergreensminiaturerailwaygmail.com

N° of Steam Locos: 10
N° of Other Locos: 14
N° of Members: 32
Approx N° of Visitors P.A.: Not known
Gauge: 5 inches and 7¼ inches

This photograph shown above is of the old site in Stickney.

GENERAL INFORMATION

Nearest Mainline Station: Boston (12 miles)
Nearest Bus Station: Spilsby (4 miles)
Car Parking: Available on site
Coach Parking: None
Food & Drinks: Available

SPECIAL INFORMATION

Originally based in Stickney, the Railway has recently had to relocate to a new site in Keal Cotes. The new site is a 4½ acre field which has been named Dawn Bank and members hope to have a basic track up and running during 2018.

OPERATING INFORMATION

Opening Times: Trains would normally operate on the last Saturday of the month from April to October as well as New Year's Day and Easter Saturday with trains running from 10.30am to 4.00pm. However, as the track on the new site is not yet up and running, no operational dates have yet been set for 2018. Please check the web site for further news.
Steam Working: Most operating days.
Prices: Admission £3.00
  Family tickets £8.00 (2 adults + 2 children)
Note: The prices shown include unlimited rides.

Detailed Directions by Car:
The railway is situated in Keal Cotes, on the A16 between Boston and Spilsby. Upon reaching Keal Cotes, turn into Fen Road opposite The Coach House pub. Continue along Fen Road to the East Fen Catchwater Drain bridge and turn right immediately after crossing the bridge. Dawn Bank is along this road – look out for the A-frame sign.

FRIMLEY LODGE MINIATURE RAILWAY

Address: Frimley Lodge Park, Sturt Road,
Frimley Green, Surrey   GU16 6HT
Phone Nº: 07710 606461 (Please use on
operating days only)
Year Formed: 1991
Location of Line: Frimley Green
Length of Line: 1 kilometre

Nº of Steam Locos: 5 (Members' locos)
Nº of Other Locos: 3
Nº of Members: Approximately 60
Approx Nº of Visitors P.A.: 20,000+
Gauge: 3½ inches, 5 inches & 7¼ inches
Web site: www.flmr.org

GENERAL INFORMATION

Nearest Mainline Station: Frimley or Ashvale (both
2 miles)
Nearest Bus Station: Farnborough (4 miles) – Take
the Number 3 bus between Aldershot and Yately.
Car Parking: Available on site
Coach Parking: Available by prior arrangement
Food & Drinks: Cafe in the Park

SPECIAL INFORMATION

The Railway is operated by volunteers from the
Frimley and Ascot Locomotive Club who bring their
own Locomotives to give pleasure to others. All the
proceeds are used for the maintenance of the
Railway and to benefit local charities.

OPERATING INFORMATION

Opening Times: 2018 dates: The first Sunday of
the month from April to November. Also on 28th
May and 27th August. Halloween trains run on 31st
October (5.30pm to 8.30pm pre-booking required)
and Santa Specials run on 9th December 11.30am to
2.30pm, also by pre-booked tickets. Trains run from
11.00am to 5.00pm on Sundays and from 11.00am
to 1.00pm then 2.00pm to 4.00pm on Wednesdays
during the school holidays.
Steam Working: Operational Sundays only.
Prices: Single Rides £1.00
        Double Rides £1.50
        Family Ticket £10.00 (14 rides)

Detailed Directions by Car:
Exit the M3 at Junction 4 and take the A331 towards Guildford. Leave the A331 at the turn-off for Mytchett and
turn left at the top of the ramp then left again at the Miners Arms into Sturt Road. Cross over the bridge then turn
right into Frimley Lodge Park. Once in the Park turn right then right again then take the next left for the Railway.

GOLDING SPRING MINIATURE RAILWAY

Address: Quainton Road Station,
Quainton, Aylesbury, Bucks.   HP22 4BY
Phone N°: (01296) 623540 (Secretary)
Year Formed: 1972
Location: Within the Buckinghamshire
Railway Centre site
Length of Line: 1,200 yards

N° of Steam Locos: 12
N° of Other Locos: 4
N° of Members: Approximately 120
Approx N° of Visitors P.A.: 25,000
Gauge: 3½ inches, 5 inches & 7¼ inches
Web site: www.vames.org.uk

GENERAL INFORMATION

Nearest Mainline Station: Aylesbury (6 miles)
Nearest Bus Station: Aylesbury (6 miles)
Car Parking: Free parking for 500 cars available
Coach Parking: Free parking for 10 coaches
Souvenir Shop(s): Yes
Food & Drinks: Yes

SPECIAL INFORMATION

The Golding Spring Miniature Railway is operated
by members of the Vale of Aylesbury Model
Engineering Society and is located at the
Buckinghamshire Railway Centre. Other attractions
include a 32mm and 45mm Garden Railway.

OPERATING INFORMATION

Opening Times: Sundays and Bank Holidays from
March to October inclusive. Also on Wednesdays in
the school holidays to coincide with the Bucks
Railway Centre. Trains run from 10.30am to 5.30pm
Steam Working: Every operational day.
Prices: £1.00 per ride
            Under-3s travel free of charge

Detailed Directions by Car:
The Buckinghamshire Railway Centre is signposted off the A41 Aylesbury to Bicester Road at Waddesdon and off
the A413 Buckingham to Aylesbury road at Whitchurch. Junctions 7, 8 and 9 of the M40 are all close by.

GREAT COCKCROW RAILWAY

Address: Hardwick Lane, Lyne,
near Chertsey, Surrey KT16 0AD
Telephone Nº: (01932) 565474 (Sundays)
Year Formed: 1968
Location of Line: Lyne, near Chertsey
Length of Line: 2 miles

Nº of Steam Locos: Approximately 25
Nº of Other Locos: 3
Approx Nº of Visitors P.A.: 10,000
Gauge: 7¼ inches
Web site: www.cockcrow.co.uk

GENERAL INFORMATION

Nearest Mainline Station: Chertsey (30 min. walk)
Nearest Bus Stop: Chertsey (30 minute walk)
Car Parking: Available on site
Coach Parking: Limited parking available on site
Souvenir Shop(s): None
Food & Drinks: Available

SPECIAL INFORMATION

Emanating from the Greywood Central Railway,
built from 1946, at a private address in Walton-on-
Thames, the Great Cockcrow Railway opened in
1968 and has continually grown since moving to its
present site. The Railway offers a choice of two
regular routes, each served every few minutes.

OPERATING INFORMATION

Opening Times: 2018 dates: Sundays from 6th May
to 28th October when trains run from 1.30pm to
4.45pm. Also open on Wednesdays in August
(1.00pm to 4.00pm) and on Halloween Saturday
27th October (5.00pm to 8.00pm).
Steam Working: Every operating day.
Prices: Various combinations of tickets are
available ranging from £4.50 for an ordinary adult
return to £20.00 for a family double return.

Detailed Directions by Car:
Exit the M25 at Junction 11 and take the A320 towards Woking. At the first roundabout take the exit towards
Chertsey and continue along this road passing St. Peter's Hospital on the left, then turn next left (B386) towards
Windlesham. Turn right almost immediately into Hardwick Lane and the railway on the right after about ¼ mile
just after Hardwick Farm.   Satellite Navigation: KT16 0AD

Grimsby & Cleethorpes M.E.S.

Address: Waltham Windmill Site, Brigsley Road, Waltham, Grimsby DN32 0JZ
Telephone Nº: None
Year Formed: 1935
Location: Waltham, near Grimsby
Length of Line: 1,300 feet for 7¼ and 5 inch gauges, 600 feet for 3½ gauge

Nº of Steam Locos: 1 (+ members' locos)
Nº of Other Locos: 2
Nº of Members: Approximately 80
Approx Nº of Visitors P.A.: 10,000
Gauge: 3½ inches, 5 inches & 7¼ inches
Web site: www.gcmes.com

GENERAL INFORMATION

Nearest Mainline Station: Grimsby Town (3 miles)
Nearest Bus Station: Grimsby (3 miles)
Car Parking: Available on site
Coach Parking: Limited space available but can be accommodated
Food & Drinks: Available at the Windmill site

SPECIAL INFORMATION

The Society's track is based in Waltham, on the outskirts of Grimsby, next to a preserved windmill dating back to 1878 (the third built on the site since 1666!) which still operates from time to time.

OPERATING INFORMATION

Opening Times: 2018 dates: Sundays and Bank Holidays from 25th March to 28th October. Trains run from 12.00pm to 4.00pm (10.00am when the Windmill Preservation Society holds special events). A special three-day open gala is held over the August Bank Holiday weekend. The railway also runs on Boxing Day and New Year's Day, from 11.00am to 3.00pm, in aid of local charities.
Steam Working: Most operating days.
Prices: From 50p per ride

Detailed Directions by Car:
The Railway is situated by Waltham Windmill on the B1203 Grimsby to Binbrook Road and is well signposted. The B1203 connects to the A16 at Scartho, a suburb of Grimsby, about a mile from the railway or to the A18 at Ashby Top, about 3 miles away.

GROSVENOR PARK MINIATURE RAILWAY

Address: Grosvenor Park, Chester, CH1 1QQ
Telephone Nº: 07530 397079
Year Formed: 1996
Location of Line:
Length of Line: 340 yards

Nº of Steam Locos: None at present
Nº of Other Locos: 2
Approx Nº of Visitors P.A.: 60,000
Gauge: 7¼ inches
Web site: None

GENERAL INFORMATION

Nearest Mainline Station: Chester (¾ mile)
Nearest Bus Station: Chester (½ mile)
Car Parking: Park & Ride or Public car parks only
Coach Parking: None
Souvenir Shop(s): Yes
Food & Drinks: Available in the Park Cafe

SPECIAL INFORMATION

Grosvenor Park railway was built in 1996 to commemorate the centenary of the Duke of Westminster's railway at nearby Eaton Hall and is located just a few minutes walk from Chester's historic city centre.

OPERATING INFORMATION

Opening Times: Weekends throughout the year and daily during the school holidays (except Christmas Day). Also on Tuesdays and Thursdays in June and July from 12.00pm to 4.30pm. Otherwise, trains run from 10.30am to 5.00pm at weekends and during the school holidays (11.00am to 4.00pm during the Winter months).
Steam Working: Sundays only.
Prices: Adults £1.50 (3 ride tickets £2.75)
Children £1.00 (3 ride tickets £1.75)
Family £3.50 (3 ride tickets £7.00)

Detailed Directions by Car:
From All Parts: Grosvenor Park is situated in the centre of Chester, by Grosvenor Park Road and about 400 yards from the City Centre. The Roman Amphitheatre is adjacent to the Park.

HALTON MINIATURE RAILWAY

Address: Palace Fields, Town Park, Runcorn WA7 6PT
Telephone N°: (01928) 701965
Year Formed: 1979
Location of Line: Runcorn
Length of Line: 1 mile approximately

N° of Steam Locos: Members locos only
N° of Other Locos: 4
N° of Members: Approximately 25
Annual Membership Fee: £11.00
Approx N° of Visitors P.A.: 12,500
Gauge: 7¼ inches
Website: www.haltonminiaturerailway.co.uk

GENERAL INFORMATION

Nearest Mainline Station: Runcorn East (¾ mile)
Nearest Bus Station: Runcorn (¾ mile)
Car Parking: Available on site
Coach Parking: Available
Souvenir Shop(s): None
Food & Drinks: Available at the adjacent Ski Centre

SPECIAL INFORMATION

The railway is operated by the Halton Miniature Railway Society and one of their locomotives, the Norton Priory (illustrated above), was built by schoolchildren from Norton Priory Secondary School in 1983! It has recently been restored to its former glory and is again in regular service.

OPERATING INFORMATION

Opening Times: Weekends and Bank Holidays from April to September plus Thursdays in August. Trains run from 1.30pm to 4.30pm.
Steam Working: Occasional dates only. Please contact the railway for further details.
Prices: Adults £1.00
Children £1.00

Detailed Directions by Car:
From All Parts: Exit the M56 at Junction 11 and follow the brown tourist signs for the Ski Centre which is adjacent to the railway.

HILCOTE VALLEY RAILWAY

Address: Fletchers Garden Centre, Bridge Farm, Stone Road, Eccleshall, ST21 6JY **Telephone Nº:** (01785) 851057 **Year Formed:** 1993 **Location of Line:** Eccleshall, Staffordshire **Length of Line:** 500 yards	**Nº of Steam Locos:** 2 **Nº of Other Locos:** 2 **Approx Nº of Visitors P.A.:** 5,000+ **Gauge:** 7¼ inches **Web site:** www.fletchersgardencentre.com

GENERAL INFORMATION

Nearest Mainline Station: Stafford (6 miles)
Nearest Bus Station: Stafford (6 miles)
Car Parking: Available on site
Coach Parking: Available
Souvenir Shop(s): None
Food & Drinks: Available on site

SPECIAL INFORMATION

Railway enthusiast Roger Greatrex designed and built this railway himself!

OPERATING INFORMATION

Opening Times: Weekends and Bank Holidays from Good Friday to the end of October and also open during the School Holidays. Trains run from 11.00am to 4.00pm.
Steam Working: Sundays only.
Prices: One ride £1.50
Three rides £4.00

Detailed Directions by Car:
From All Parts: Exit the M6 at Junction 14 and take the A5013 to Eccleshall. Just after the junction with the A519, turn right onto the B5026 Stone Road and the Garden Centre is on the right at Bridge Farm after ¾ mile.

HOLLYBUSH MINIATURE RAILWAY

Address: Hollybush Garden Centre,
Warstone Road, Shareshill,
Wolverhampton   WV10 7LX
Telephone Nº: (01922) 418050
Year Formed: 1996
Location of Line: Wolverhampton
Length of Line: 950 yards

Nº of Steam Locos: None
Nº of Other Locos: 2
Approx Nº of Visitors P.A.: Not known
Gauge: 7¼ inches
Web site: www.hollybush-garden.com/
miniature-railway/

GENERAL INFORMATION

Nearest Mainline Station: Cannock (4 miles)
Nearest Bus Station: Cannock (4 miles)
Car Parking: Available on site
Coach Parking: Available
Souvenir Shop(s): Yes
Food & Drinks: Available

OPERATING INFORMATION

Opening Times: Wednesday to Sunday from Easter
to early September and daily during the School
Holidays. Also weekends from September to March.
Trains run from 10.00am to 4.30pm (until 4.15pm
on Sundays).
Steam Working: None at present.
Prices: Adults £2.00
          Children £1.50 (Under-2s ride free)

Detailed Directions by Car:
From All Parts: Exit the M6 at Junction 11 and follow the brown tourist signs onto the A462 for the railway
which is on the left after approximately 600 yards.

HOLLYCOMBE – STEAM IN THE COUNTRY

Address: Iron Hill, Midhurst Road, Liphook, Hants. GU30 7LP
Telephone Nº: (01428) 724900
Year Formed: 1971
Location of Line: Hollycombe, Liphook
Length of Line: 1½ miles of 2 feet gauge and a third of a mile of 7¼ inch gauge

Nº of Steam Locos: 2
Nº of Other Locos: 2
Approx Nº of Visitors P.A.: 25,000
Gauge: 2 feet and 7¼ inches
Web site: www.hollycombe.co.uk

GENERAL INFORMATION

Nearest Mainline Station: Liphook (1 mile)
Nearest Bus Station: Liphook
Car Parking: Extensive grass area
Coach Parking: Hardstanding
Souvenir Shop(s): Yes
Food & Drinks: Yes – Cafe

SPECIAL INFORMATION

The narrow gauge railway ascends to spectacular views of the Downs and is part of an extensive working steam museum.

OPERATING INFORMATION

Opening Times: 2018 dates: Sundays and Bank Holidays from Easter until the 14th October and also for a number of Special Event days. Open daily from 31st July to 27th August (closed on other Mondays in August but for 27th). Please check the web site for further details. The Museum opens 11.00am to 5.00pm with rides starting at 12.30pm.
Steam Working: Please contact the museum for further information.
Prices: Adult £16.00
Child £12.00
Senior Citizen £14.00
Family £50.00 (2 adults + 2 children)
Family £60.00 (2 adults + 3 children)

Detailed Directions by Car:
Take the A3 to Liphook and follow the brown tourist signs for the museum.

HULL & DISTRICT S.M.E.E.

Address: c/o 17 Orchard Close, Anlaby, Hull   HU10 6RF
Phone Nº: None
Year Formed: 1937
Location of Line: West Park, Hull
Length of Line: 190 metres (raised track) and 400 metres (ground level track)
Web site: www.finnaj.karoo.net/hdsmee.html

Nº of Steam Locos: Approximately 15
Nº of Other Locos: Approximately 10
Nº of Members: Approximately 60
Approx Nº of Visitors P.A.: 5,000
Gauge: 2½ inches, 3½ inches & 5 inches on the raised track; 5 inches & 7¼ inches on the ground level track

GENERAL INFORMATION

Nearest Mainline Station: Hull Paragon (1½ miles)
Nearest Bus Station: Hull Central (1½ miles)
Car Parking: Available on site
Coach Parking: None
Food & Drinks: None

SPECIAL INFORMATION

The Hull & District Society of Model & Experimental Engineers operates a railway in West Park in Hull.

OPERATING INFORMATION

Opening Times: Passenger services run on Sundays from 12.00pm until 3.00pm, Easter to October, subject to the weather and staff availability. The railway also operates on some Wednesday afternoons during the school holidays. Please contact the railway for further information.
Steam Working: Whenever available.
Prices: Train rides are 30p per person but additional donations to aid in upkeep are always welcome.

Detailed Directions by Car:
From the West, take the M62 to Hull where it becomes the A63. Continue along the A63 (Clive Sullivan Way) then turn left into Rawling Way following the signs for Hull Royal Infirmary. After ½ mile turn left onto Anlaby Road (A1105) then right after ½ mile into Walton Street. Turn right into West Park then right again for the Railway.

ICKENHAM MINIATURE RAILWAY

Correspondence: 25 Copthall Road East, Ickenham, Middlesex UB10 8SD **Telephone Nº:** (01895) 630125 **Year Formed:** 1948 **Location:** At the rear of the "Coach and Horses" Public House, Ickenham **Length of Line:** 1,100 feet	**Nº of Steam Locos:** Up to 6 **Nº of Other Locos:** Up to 6 **Nº of Members:** Approximately 70 **Approx Nº of Visitors P.A.:** 9,000 **Gauge:** 3½ inches and 5 inches **Web site:** www.idsme.co.uk

GENERAL INFORMATION

Nearest Mainline Station: West Ruislip (½ mile)
Nearest Underground Station: Ickenham (¼ mile)
Car Parking: Public car park is adjacent
Coach Parking: None
Food & Drinks: Available

SPECIAL INFORMATION

The Railway is operated by volunteers from the Ickenham & District Society of Model Engineers.

OPERATING INFORMATION

Opening Times: The first Saturday of the month from April to December inclusive. Trains run from 12.00pm to 5.30pm (or until dusk later in the year).
Steam Working: All operating days subject to availability.
Prices: 80p per ride.

Detailed Directions by Car:
The Railway is located in Ickenham Village behind the Coach and Horses Public House which is adjacent to the junction of the B466 Ickenham High Road, B466 Long Lane and the B467 Swakeleys Road. From the East: Exit the A40 at Hillingdon Circus turning right onto the B466 Long Lane towards Ickenham/Ruislip. Continue for 1 mile and turn right into Community Close for the car park just before the Coach and Horses in the centre of Ickenham; From the West: Exit the A40 at Hillingdon Circus turning left onto B466 Long Lane. Then as above.

ILFORD & WEST ESSEX MODEL RAILWAY CLUB

Address: Station Road, Chadwell Heath, Romford, Essex RM6 4BU
Telephone Nº: (01708) 701290
Year Formed: 1930
Location of Line: Chadwell Heath
Length of Line: 150 yards

Nº of Steam Locos: 2
Nº of Other Locos: 3
Nº of Members: Approximately 50
Approx Nº of Visitors P.A.: 400
Gauge: 7¼ inches
Web site: www.iwemrc.org.uk

GENERAL INFORMATION

Nearest Mainline Station: Chadwell Heath (adjacent)
Nearest Bus Station: Chadwell Heath (100 yards)
Car Parking: None on site but a public car park is 100 yards away
Coach Parking: None
Food & Drinks: Light refreshments are available

SPECIAL INFORMATION

The Ilford & West Essex Model Railway Club was formed in 1930 and as such is one of the oldest clubs of its type in the country. Please note that access to the site is by steps only and it is therefore not suitable for wheelchairs.

OPERATING INFORMATION

Opening Times: The first Sunday of the month from April to September inclusive.
Please contact the railway for further information. Trains run from 10.30am to 4.00pm.
Steam Working: When available.
Prices: 50p per ride or £3.00 for an all-day pass

Detailed Directions by Car:
The site is alongside Chadwell Heath mainline station just off the A118 between Romford and Ilford town centres. Station Road is to the South of the A118 approximately half-way between the two towns. The site itself is approximately 200 yards down Station Road with a car park on the right hand side.

KINVER & WEST MIDLANDS S.M.E.

Correspondence: Mr P. Hardwick,
43 Nightingale Drive, Tipton   DY4 7QL
Telephone Nº: (0121) 520-0472
Year Formed: 1961
Location of Line: Marsh Playing Fields,
Kinver, Staffordshire
Length of Line: ½ mile

Nº of Steam Locos: Members locos only
Nº of Other Locos: Members locos only
Nº of Members: Approximately 100
Gauge: 3½ inches and 5 inches
Website: www.kinvermodelengineers.org.uk
E-mail: peterhatkinversme@gmail.com

GENERAL INFORMATION

Nearest Mainline Station: Kidderminster (6 miles)
Nearest Bus Station: Stourbridge (3 miles)
Car Parking: Available on site
Coach Parking: Available on site
Food & Drinks: None

SPECIAL INFORMATION

The Kinver & West Midlands Society of Model
Engineers dates back to organisations formed in the
1920s and has operated a railway in Kinver since
1962. In addition to the main 3½ and 5 inch line, a
short 7¼ inch track is now in operation at the site.

OPERATING INFORMATION

Opening Times: Most Sunday afternoons between
Easter and October, weather permitting. Trains run
between 2.00pm and approximately 4.30pm. Please
check the web site for further information.
Steam Working: Most operating days.
Prices: £1.00 per ride.

Detailed Directions by Car:
The Society's tracksite is situated on the Marsh Playing Fields at the end of the High Street in the village of Kinver
which is to the West of Stourbridge and to the North of Kidderminster.

LANGFORD & BEELEIGH RAILWAY

Address: Museum of Power, Hatfield Road, Langford, Maldon, Essex, CM9 6QA **Telephone Nº**: (01621) 843183 **Year Formed**: 2003 **Length of Line**: ¼ mile loop	**Nº of Steam Locos**: 4 **Nº of Other Locos**: 1 **Nº of Members**: 140 (12 actively involved) **Approx Nº of Visitors P.A.**: 6,000 **Gauge**: 7¼ inches **Web site**: www.museumofpower.org.uk

GENERAL INFORMATION

Nearest Mainline Station: Witham (4 miles)
Nearest Bus Station: Chelmsford (6 miles)
Car Parking: Available on site
Coach Parking: Available
Souvenir Shop(s): Yes
Food & Drinks: Available

SPECIAL INFORMATION

The Railway is situated at the Museum of Power which is housed in the Steam Pumping Station at Langford in Essex. The Museum was set up to exhibit and demonstrate working examples of power sources of all types and chronicle the major roles that they have played in history.

OPERATING INFORMATION

Opening Times: 2018 dates: 1st April; 20th May; 10th June; 15th July; 5th & 19th August; 2nd & 16th September; 7th October; Also 9th December for pre-booked Santa Specials. Please contact the Museum for further information.
Steam Working: On all operating days.
Prices: £1.00 per ride (6 rides for £5.00)
Note: Admission to the Museum is an extra charge.

Detailed Directions by Car:
The Museum is situated in Langford, on the B1019 Maldon to Hatfield Peverel Road. From the A12, take the Hatfield Peverel exit, pass through the village and take the B1019 Hatfield Road towards Ulting & Maldon. The Museum is on the right hand side after approximately 3 miles on the outskirts of Langford.

LEICESTER SOCIETY OF MODEL ENGINEERS

Address: Abbey Park, Leicester LE1 3EJ
Telephone Nº: (0116) 247-9844
Year Formed: 1909 (located at Abbey Park since 1951)
Location of Line: Victorian Public Park
Length of Line: 874 yards
Web site: www.lsme.uk.com

Nº of Steam Locos: Members locos only
Nº of Other Locos: 5 diesels
Nº of Members: 100+
Annual Membership Fee: £30.00
Approx Nº of Visitors P.A.: 9,500
Gauges: 2½ inches, 3½ inches, 5 inches and 7¼ inches (Also '0' and 1 inch gauge)

GENERAL INFORMATION

Nearest Mainline Station: Leicester (1½ miles)
Nearest Bus Station: Leicester (½ mile)
Car Parking: Available at the nearby Riverside Car Park (Pay and Display)
Coach Parking: None
Souvenir Shop(s): None
Food & Drinks: Available elsewhere in the Park

SPECIAL INFORMATION

The Society has been located within Abbey Park since 1953.

OPERATING INFORMATION

Opening Times: 2018 dates: Sundays and Bank Holidays Mondays from April until 28th October. Trains run from 1.00pm to 5.00pm. Santa Specials will run on 9th December.
Steam Working: Subject to availability, otherwise diesel services.
Prices: Adults £1.00
   Children £1.00 (Under-5s ride for free)

Detailed Directions by Car:
From All Parts: The railway is located at the South-Western edge of Leicester's Abbey Park and is best accessed from the St. Margaret's Riverside car park, situated off the A6 (North) St. Margaret's Way, adjoining the inner ring-road (Burley's Way). The station is located towards the riverside end of Cave's Walk, Abbey Park.

LITTLEDOWN MINIATURE RAILWAY

Address: Littledown Park, Chaseside, Castle Lane East, Bournemouth, BH7 7DX
Contact Telephone Nº: 07879 355399
Year Formed: 1924
Location of Line: Littledown Park
Length of Line: Over one third of a mile

Nº of Steam Locos: 15+
Nº of Other Locos: 10+
Nº of Members: 140+
Approx Nº of Visitors P.A.: 4,000
Gauge: 3½ inches, 5 inches & 7¼ inches
Web site: www.littledownrailway.co.uk

GENERAL INFORMATION

Nearest Mainline Station:
Bournemouth Central (3½ miles)
Nearest Bus Station: Bournemouth
Car Parking:
In Littledown Leisure Centre car park
Coach Parking: As above

SPECIAL INFORMATION

Bournemouth and District Society of Model Engineers operate the railway at Littledown Park. The society also operates a 16mm garden railway alongside the track.

OPERATING INFO

Opening Times: Most Sundays and Wednesdays throughout the year subject to weather conditions. Trains run from 11.00am to 3.00pm.
Steam Working: Subject to availability. Please contact the railway for further information.
Prices: £1.00 per ride.

Detailed Directions by Car:
The Railway is situated at Littledown Park which is to the North-East of Bournemouth town centre close (and to the South of) the junction of Wessex Way (A338) and Castle Lane (A3060).

LITTLE HAY MINIATURE RAILWAY

Address: Balleny Green, Little Hay Lane, Little Hay WS14 0QB
Telephone Nº: None
Year Formed: 1948
Location of Line: 100 yards from the Holly Bush Public House
Length of Line: ½ mile (Ground level)

Nº of Steam Locos: 20 (approximately)
Nº of Other Locos: 4
Nº of Members: Approximately 115
Approx Nº of Visitors P.A.: 4,500
Gauge: 2½ inches, 3½ inches, 5 inches and 7¼ inches (elevated & ground level)
Web site: www.scmes.co.uk

GENERAL INFORMATION

Nearest Mainline Station: Blake Street (1½ miles)
Nearest Bus Station: Sutton Coldfield or Lichfield (each approximately 5 miles)
Car Parking: Available on site
Coach Parking: None
Food & Drinks: Food and refreshments are available at most event and open days

SPECIAL INFORMATION

The Railway is owned and operated by members of the Sutton Coldfield Model Engineering Society Ltd.

and has been based at Balleny Green since 1981. A SM32 gauge track 400 feet in length is now available and visitors can bring their own locomotives to run on it.

OPERATING INFORMATION

Opening Times: 2018 dates: 1st April; 7th & 28th May; 24th June; 1st July; 5th August; 7th October; 4th November; 2nd, 8th, 9th & 26th December. Open from 11.00am to 4.00pm on these dates.
Steam Working: All operating days.
Prices: Prices depend on the event being held.

Detailed Directions by Car:
From Lichfield: Head south on the A38 dual carriageway. Approximately ½ mile after the A38/A5 Junction, turn right at the sign for Little Hay. Follow the road past the Pumping Station and Holly Bush pub then turn left after approximately 100 yards through the steel gates set between stone pillars with lanterns to enter the railway; From the South: Heading northwards along the A38, turn left at the Little Hay sign which is located approximately 2 miles after passing the Bassets Pole Junction of the A38/A453. Then as above.

LLWYFAN CERRIG MINIATURE RAILWAY

Address: c/o Gwili Railway, Bronwydd Arms   SA33 6HT
Telephone Nº: (01267) 238213
Year Formed: 1993
Location of Line: Llwyfan Cerrig Station on the Gwili Railway
Length of Line: 300 yards

Nº of Steam Locos: None
Nº of Other Locos: 1
Nº of Members: 900 shareholders, 450 Society members (Gwili Railway)
Annual Membership Fee: £18.00
Approx Nº of Visitors P.A.: 28,000
Gauge: 7¼ inches
Web site: www.gwili-railway.co.uk

GENERAL INFORMATION

Nearest Mainline Station: Carmarthen (3 miles)
Nearest Bus Station: Carmarthen (3 miles)
Car Parking: Free parking at Bronwydd Arms
Coach Parking: Free parking at Bronwydd Arms
Souvenir Shop(s): Yes
Food & Drinks: Yes

SPECIAL INFORMATION

The railway can only be reached via the standard-gauge Gwili Railway line. The cost of rides on the miniature railway are included in the standard gauge railway fares!

OPERATING INFORMATION

Opening Times: 2018 dates: Open every weekend from 8th April to 28th October and daily during July and August. Also open on Wednesdays and Thursdays from April to October. Please phone or check the website for further details.
Steam Working: None at present
Prices: Adult £12.00   Senior Citizens £11.00
            Child £6.00 (Under-3s ride for free)
Note: The above prices are for rides on the standard gauge Gwili Railway. Miniature Railway rides are included in these prices.

Detailed Directions by Car:
Gwili Railway is three miles North of Carmarthen – signposted off the A484 Carmarthen to Cardigan Road. The Llwyfan Cerrig Miniature Railway is only accessible via the Gwili Railway Line.

MOORS VALLEY RAILWAY

Address: Moors Valley Country Park, Horton Road, Ashley Heath, Nr. Ringwood, Hants. BH24 2ET **Telephone Nº**: (01425) 471415 **Year Formed**: 1985 **Location**: Moors Valley Country Park	**Length of Line**: 1 mile **Nº of Steam Locos**: 15 **Nº of Other Locos**: 2 **Approx Nº of Visitors P.A.**: 100,000 **Gauge**: 7¼ inches **Web site**: www.moorsvalleyrailway.co.uk

GENERAL INFORMATION

Nearest Mainline Station: Bournemouth (12 miles)
Nearest Bus Station: Ringwood (3 miles)
Car Parking: Parking charges vary throughout the year. Maximum charge £9.00 per day.
Coach Parking: Charges are applied for parking
Souvenir Shop(s): Yes + Model Railway Shop
Food & Drinks: Yes

SPECIAL INFORMATION

The Moors Valley Railway is a complete small Railway with signalling and 2 signal boxes and also 4 tunnels and 2 level crossings.

OPERATING INFORMATION

Opening Times: 2018 dates: Weekends throughout the year. Daily from 26th May to 16th December and during the school holidays. Also Santa Specials in December and occasional other openings. Phone the Railways for details.
Steam Working: 10.45am to 5.00pm when open.
Prices: Adult Return £3.85
                Child Return £2.55
Special rates are available for parties of 10 or more and Day Rover tickets are available.

Detailed Directions by Car:
From All Parts: Moors Valley Country Park is situated on Horton Road which is off the A31 Ferndown to Ringwood road near the junction with the A338 to Bournemouth.

NATIONAL RAILWAY MUSEUM – YORK

Address: National Railway Museum, Leeman Road, York   YO26 4XJ
Telephone Nº: 08448 153139
Year Formed: 1975
Location of Line: York
Length of Line: 800 metres

Nº of Steam Locos: 79
Nº of Other Locos: 37
Approx Nº of Visitors P.A.: 900,000
Web site: www.nrm.org.uk

GENERAL INFORMATION

Nearest Mainline Station: York (¼ mile)
Nearest Bus Station: York (¼ mile)
Car Parking: On site long stay car park
Coach Parking: On site
Souvenir Shop(s): Yes
Food & Drinks: Excellent on-site catering facilities.

SPECIAL INFORMATION

The Museum is the greatest of its kind in the world, housing the Nation's collection of locomotives, carriages, uniforms, posters and an extensive photographic archive. Special events and exhibitions run throughout the year. The Museum is the home of the Mallard – the fastest steam locomotive in the world and Shinkansen, the only Bullet train outside of Japan.

OPERATING INFORMATION

Opening Times: Open daily 10.00am to 6.00pm (or 5.00pm during the winter months). Closed from 24th to 26th of December.
Steam Working: School holidays – please phone to confirm details
Prices: Free admission to the museum, but visitors are invited to make a donation on entry.
Rides are £3.00 each (Under-2s free of charge)
Family Tickets (up to 4 persons) are £10.00.
Under-12s must be accompanied by an adult.

Detailed Directions by Car:
The Museum is located in the centre of York, just behind the Railway Station. It is clearly signposted from all approaches to York.

NESS ISLANDS RAILWAY

Address: Whin Park, Inverness IV3 5SS	**Nº of Steam Locos**: 1
Telephone Nº: (01463) 235533	**Nº of Other Locos**: 2
Year Formed: 1983	**Approx Nº of Visitors P.A.**: 12,000
Location of Line: Inverness	**Gauge**: 7¼ inches
Length of Line: 900 yards	**Web site**: www.nessislandsrailway.co.uk

GENERAL INFORMATION

Nearest Mainline Station: Inverness (2 miles)
Nearest Bus Station: Inverness (2 miles)
Car Parking: Available on site
Coach Parking: Available
Souvenir Shop(s): Yes
Food & Drinks: None

SPECIAL INFORMATION

Ness Islands Railway is Britain's most northerly 7¼ inch gauge line.

OPERATING INFORMATION

Opening Times: 2018 dates: Weekends from Easter to the end of October and also daily during the school holidays.
Trains run from 11.30am to 4.30pm.
Steam Working: Most weekends.
Prices: Adults £2.00 per ride
Children £2.00 per ride (Under-4s free)

Detailed Directions by Car:
From All Parts: The Railway is located in Inverness, just to the south of the A82 Glenurquhart Road. Turn into Bught Road at Queens Park and the railway is on the right after a short distance.

NORTH SCARLE MINIATURE RAILWAY

Address: North Scarle Playing Field, Swinderby Road, North Scarle, Lincolnshire LN6 9ER (for SatNav)
Telephone Nº: (01427) 881698
Year Formed: 1933
Location of Line: North Scarle, between Newark and Lincoln
Length of Line: A third of a mile

Nº of Steam Locos: 7
Nº of Other Locos: 8
Nº of Members: 48
Annual Membership Fee: See web site
Approx Nº of Visitors P.A.: 3,000
Gauges: 7¼ inches and 5 inches
Web site: www.lincolnmes.co.uk

GENERAL INFORMATION

Nearest Mainline Station: Newark Northgate (5 miles)
Nearest Bus Station: Newark (5 miles)
Car Parking: 300 spaces available on site
Coach Parking: None available
Souvenir Shop(s): None
Food & Drinks: Available on special days only

SPECIAL INFORMATION

The Railway is owned and operated by the Lincoln and District Model Engineering Society which was founded in 1933.

OPERATING INFORMATION

Opening Times: Car Boot Sale Sundays only!
Dates for 2018: 1st, 15th & 29th April; 13th & 27th May; 10th & 24th June; 8th & 22nd July; 5th & 19th August; 2nd, 16th & 30th September.
Trains run from 9.00am to 12.00pm.
An open weekend is to be held on 22nd & 23rd September.
Steam Working: Every running day.
Prices: Adult Return £1.20
Child Return £1.20

Detailed Directions by Car:
North Scarle is situated off the A46 between Lincoln and Newark (about 5 miles from Newark). Alternatively, take the A1133 from Gainsborough and follow the North Scarle signs when around 6 miles from Newark.

NORTHAMPTON SOCIETY OF MODEL ENGINEERS

Contact Address: 7 Hodnet Close,
Northampton   NN4 0XY
Telephone Nº: 0790 705-1388
Year Formed: 1933
Location of Line: Lower Delapre Park,
London Road, Northampton   NN4 8AJ
Length of Line: 1,740 feet (raised track)
and 3,034 feet (ground level track)

Nº of Steam Locos: Up to 9 running
Nº of Other Locos: 4 to 6 run occasionally
Nº of Members: 145
Approx Nº of Visitors P.A.: 10,000
Gauge: 3½ inches, 5 inches & 7¼ inches
Web site: www.nsme.co.uk

GENERAL INFORMATION

Nearest Mainline Station: Northampton (2 miles)
Nearest Bus Station: Northampton (2 miles)
Car Parking: Available on site
Coach Parking: On London Road
Food & Drinks: Light refreshments are available

SPECIAL INFORMATION

The Northampton Society of Model Engineers is a
long established society with excellent facilities for
model engineers. The society has over 120 members
with wide ranging interests, several of whom have
won major awards at National exhibitions.

The two tracks were extended during 2011 and are
located in a woodland setting with a new garden
railway and a picnic site. The site may be hired for
Birthday parties on Tuesdays and Saturdays.
Please check the web site for further information.

OPERATING INFORMATION

Opening Times: May Day Bank Holiday Monday
then the first Sunday of the month thereafter up to
and including October. Trains run from 2.00pm to
5.00pm.
Steam Working: Every operating day.
Prices: 50p per ride.

Detailed Directions by Car:
From the M1: Exit at Junction 15 and take the A508 to Northampton. Take the 2nd turn off onto the A45 (for the
Town Centre) and then the 2nd exit at the roundabout. After ½ mile turn right just before the pelican crossing
and immediately turn left through the steel gate onto the access track for the railway; From the East: Follow the
A45 and take the turn off signposted for Daventry and the Town Centre. Take the 4th exit at the roundabout onto
the A508, then as above; From the Town Centre: Take the A508 South (Bridge Street). Cross the river and go
straight on at the traffic lights. Pass a petrol station on the left and immediately after the pelican crossing turn left
then immediately left again for the railway.

NORWICH & DISTRICT S.M.E.

Correspondence: emprinfo@ndsme.co.uk
Telephone Nº: None
Year Formed: 1933
Location of Line: Eaton Park, Norwich
Length of Line: Two tracks – 'Mainline' is 800 metres (7¼ and 5 inch gauges) and the 'Heritage Track' is 955 feet (raised 5 and 3½ inch gauges)

Nº of Steam Locos: 2 + visiting locos
Nº of Other Locos: 2
Nº of Members: Approximately 100
Approx Nº of Visitors P.A.: 16,000
Gauge: 3½ inches, 5 inches & 7¼ inches
Web site: www.ndsme.org

GENERAL INFORMATION

Nearest Mainline Station: Norwich (3 miles)
Nearest Bus Station: Norwich (2 miles)
Car Parking: Available in Eaton Park
Coach Parking: None
Food & Drinks: Available in Eaton Park

SPECIAL INFORMATION

Norwich & District Society of Model Engineers was formed in 1933 and operates two tracks in Eaton Park. The 'Mainline' is a 7¼ inch and 5 inch ground level track and the 'Heritage Track' is a raised tracking using 5 inch and 3½ inch gauges.

OPERATING INFORMATION

Opening Times: 2018 dates: Sundays and Bank Holidays from 1st April to 23rd September. Trains run from 1.00pm to 5.00pm, weather permitting.
Steam Working: Most operating days
Prices: £1.00 per ride on the 'Mainline'
50p per ride on the 'Heritage Track'

Detailed Directions by Car:
Take the A11 or A140 into Norwich and upon reaching the ring road, turn left. At the second set of traffic lights turn left into South Park Avenue and the entrance to Eaton Park is on the right hand side.
Alternative route: Take the A47 into Norwich and turn right at the ring road. At the 3rd set of traffic lights turn right into South Park Avenue.

PICNIC FIELD RAILWAY

Correspondence: c/o 21 Talisman Street, Hitchin SG4 0EZ
Telephone Nº: 07758 121338
Year Formed: 1980
Location: Audley End Miniature Railway
Length of Line: 1,300 feet
Nº of Steam Locos: Several members' locos

Nº of Other Locos: 2 + members' locos
Nº of Members: 60
Approx Nº of Visitors P.A.: 12,000
Gauge: 5 inches and 7¼ inches
Web site: www.swdsme.org.uk
E-mail: swdsme@outlook.com

GENERAL INFORMATION

Nearest Mainline Station: Audley End (1 mile)
Nearest Bus Station: Saffron Walden (1 mile)
Car Parking: On site plus further overflow parking
Coach Parking: Available by prior arrangement with the Audley End Railway
Souvenir Shop(s): Yes – at the Audley End Railway
Food & Drinks: Yes – at the Audley End Railway

SPECIAL INFORMATION

The Saffron Walden & District Society of Model Engineers operates the "Picnic Field Railway" in the grounds of the 10¼ inch Audley End Steam Railway, opposite Audley End House. Visitors are required to buy an Audley End Railway admission ticket for access to the site.

OPERATING INFORMATION

Opening Times: Most weekends when the Audley End Railway is open, from Easter to October and on selected other dates. The club also holds a number of events throughout the year. Please check the website of the SWDSME for further details, or write to the correspondence address above.
Steam Working: Various dates throughout the year.
Prices: £1.00 per ride (A Multi-ride ticket is £3.00)
Note: Visitors need to buy an Audley End Railway admission ticket for access to the site.

Detailed Directions by Car:
Exit the M11 at Junction 10 if southbound or Junction 9 if northbound and follow the signs for Audley End House. The railway is situated just across the road from Audley End House.

PINEWOOD MINIATURE RAILWAY

Address: Pinewood Leisure Centre, Old Wokingham Road, Wokingham, Berkshire RG40 3AQ
Phone Nº: None
Year Formed: 1984
Location: Pinewood Leisure Centre
Length of Line: 800 metres

Nº of Steam Locos: 20 (All owned
Nº of Other Locos: 20   by Members)
Nº of Members: Approximately 40
Annual Membership Fee: £50.00
Approx Nº of Visitors P.A.: 3,000
Gauge: 5 inches and 7¼ inches
Web site: www.pinewoodrailway.co.uk

GENERAL INFORMATION

Nearest Mainline Station: Bracknell
Nearest Bus Station: Bracknell
Car Parking: Available on site
Coach Parking: Available by arrangement
Souvenir Shop(s): None
Food & Drinks: Light refreshments are available

SPECIAL INFORMATION

The Pinewood Miniature Railway runs through attractive woodlands backing on to a Leisure Centre.

OPERATING INFORMATION

Opening Times: 2018 dates: Public running on the 3rd Sunday in the month from March to October. Santa Specials on the first two Sundays in December (pre-booking is required for these dates). Private Parties can sometimes be catered for by prior arrangement. Trains run from 1.30pm to 4.00pm.
Steam Working: All open days.
Prices: £1.00 per ride or 6 rides for £5.00

Detailed Directions by Car:
From the M3 or the A30 take the A322 towards Bracknell. Once on the A322, keep in the left hand lane to the first major roundabout then take the first exit onto the B3430 towards Wokingham along Nine Mile Ride. Cross the next roundabout (A3095) and continue on the B3430 passing the Golden Retriever pub and the Crematorium. Go straight on at the next mini-roundabout then turn right at the following roundabout into Old Wokingham Road. The Pinewood Leisure Centre is on the left after approximately 100 metres.

PLYMOUTH MINIATURE STEAM

Address: Goodwin Park, Pendeen Crescent, Southway, Plymouth PL6 6RE	**N° of Steam Locos**: 2 + member locos
	N° of Other Locos: 2 + member locos
Phone N°: (01752) 661780 (Secretary)	**N° of Members**: Approximately 100
Year Formed: 1970	**Approx N° of Visitors P.A.**: 2,000
Location of Line: Goodwin Park Public Nature Reserve	**Gauge**: 3½ inches, 5 inches & 7¼ inches
	Web site:
Length of Line: ½ mile	www.plymouthminiaturesteam.co.uk

GENERAL INFORMATION

Nearest Mainline Station: Plymouth (6 miles)
Nearest Bus Station: Plymouth (6 miles)
Car Parking: Available on site (limited headroom)
Coach Parking: None
Food & Drinks: Light refreshments available.

SPECIAL INFORMATION

The railway runs through Goodwin Park, a site specially developed by members of the Society which was opened in 1990 and has since been designated as a Public Nature Reserve.

OPERATING INFORMATION

Opening Times: Open during the 1st and 3rd Sunday afternoons of each month from April to October inclusive, from 2.00pm to 4.30pm.
Steam Working: Most operating days.
Prices: 75p per ride.

Detailed Directions by Car:
From the A38 Plymouth Parkway, follow the signs for Tavistock (A386) travelling North until reaching a new road junction near Plymouth Airport and a Park & Ride site. Turn left at this junction into the Southway Estate and follow the road for ½ mile past two mini-roundabouts and a set of traffic lights. At the 3rd mini-roundabout turn left into Pendeen Crescent and about 200 yard on the right is a signpost for the railway. Follow the lane to the parking area but please note that the bridge has just 6 feet headroom so large vehicles must park outside the track!

POPLAR MINIATURE RAILWAY

Address: Poplar Nurseries, Coggleshall Road, Marks Tey, Near Colchester, CO6 1HR
Telephone Nº: (01206) 210374
Year Formed: 2013
Location: Poplar Garden Centre

Length of Line: 370 yards
Nº of Steam Locos: 3
Nº of Other Locos: 1
Approx Nº of Visitors P.A.: 49,000
Gauge: 7¼ inches
Web site: www.poplarrailway.co.uk

GENERAL INFORMATION

Nearest Mainline Station: Marks Tey (1½ miles)
Nearest Bus Station: Colchester (8 miles) – Service 70 from Colchester to Braintree runs past the site.
Car Parking: Available on site
Coach Parking: Available on site
Souvenir Shop(s): Available
Food & Drinks: Restaurant available on site

SPECIAL INFORMATION

The Railway runs through the gardens of Poplar Nurseries and complements the other attractions of the garden centre which include a restaurant, farm shop and play area.

OPERATING INFORMATION

Opening Times: 2018 dates: Weekends and daily during local School Holidays throughout the year (from 11.00am until 4.00pm) but closed between 1st January and the February Half Term holidays. Open daily from 18th July to 2nd September and also for special Halloween and Christmas events in October and December respectively. Please contact the railway for details of these Special Events. From April to September the railway is also open Wednesday to Friday between 10.30am to 2.00pm.
Steam Working: Most operating days.
Prices: £2.00 per person for the first ride then £1.00 for each additional ride that day. Under-4s travel free of charge but must be accompanied by an adult. Special Travel Cards offering 10 or 20 rides for regular visitors are available.

Detailed Directions by Car:
From the M11, Stansted and the North: Exit the M11 at Junction 8 and follow the A120 to Marks Tey. Poplar Nurseries is situated on the right hand side of the road; From London and the South: Take the A12 for Colchester then turn off onto the A120 at Junction 25. Follow the A120 and Stansted Airport signs for 1 mile from the junction and Poplar Nurseries is located on the left hand side of the road.

PORTERSWICK JUNCTION LIGHT RAILWAY

Address: Hidden Valley Discovery Park, Tredidon St. Thomas, Launceston, Cornwall PL15 8SJ
Telephone Nº: (01566) 86463
Year Formed: 2003
Location of Line: Near Launceston
Length of Line: 1 mile

Nº of Steam Locos: None
Nº of Other Locos: 1
Approx Nº of Visitors P.A.: 26,000
Gauge: 7¼ inches
Web site: www.hiddenvalleydiscoverypark.co.uk

GENERAL INFORMATION

Nearest Mainline Station: Liskeard (16 miles)
Nearest Bus Station: Launceston (4 miles)
Car Parking: Available on site
Coach Parking: Available on site
Souvenir Shop(s): Yes
Food & Drinks: Available

SPECIAL INFORMATION

The railway is situated in Hidden Valley Discovery Park which contains a number of other attractions including various trails, mazes and new landscaped gardens.

OPERATING INFORMATION

Opening Times: 2018 dates: Daily from 26th March to 15th September and also during October half-term. Open from 10.00am to 5.00pm with the last admission at 2.00pm each day.
Steam Working: None at present.
Prices: Adult £9.95
Child £8.95 (Free for ages 4 and under)
Concession £7.95

Note: The above prices are for entry into the Park which includes the cost of train rides.

Detailed Directions by Car:
Take the A30 from Exeter towards Bodmin and then (shortly after Launceston) take the A395 towards Davidstow and Bude. After about one mile, turn right following the brown tourist signs for 'Hidden Valley'. The railway is located in the Discovery Park approximately ¾ mile along this road.

PORTHMADOG WOODLAND RAILWAY

Address: Tremadog Road, Porthmadog, Gwynedd LL49 9DY
Telephone Nº: (01766) 513402
Year Formed: 1961
Location of Line: At the Welsh Highland Heritage Railway
Length of Line: 550 yards

Nº of Steam Locos: 3 (at the WHR)
Nº of Other Locos: 18 (at the WHR)
Nº of Members: 1,000
Annual Membership Fee: £30.00 Adult
Approx Nº of Visitors P.A.: 25,000
Gauge: 7¼ inches
Web site: www.whr.co.uk

GENERAL INFORMATION

Nearest Mainline Station: Porthmadog (adjacent)
Nearest Bus Station: Services 1 & 3 stop 50 yards away
Car Parking: Free parking at site, plus a public Pay and Display car park within 100 yards
Coach Parking: Adjacent
Souvenir Shop(s): Yes – large range available
Food & Drinks: Yes – excellent home cooking at the Russell Team Room!

SPECIAL INFORMATION

The Porthmadog Woodland Railway is located at the Welsh Highland Heritage Railway. Tickets for the WHHR entitle customers to free rides on the Woodland Railway.

OPERATING INFORMATION

Opening Times: 2018 dates: Daily from 28th April to 3rd November except for Mondays and Fridays in May, June, September & October. Also open daily during local school holidays and at weekends during April. Trains run from 10.30am to 4.00pm.
Steam Working: Most days during the School Holidays and on other selected weekends. Please check with the railway for further details.
Prices: Adult Day Rover £8.95
Child Day Rover £4.50 (Under-5s free)
Family Day Rover £22.50
(2 adults + 2 children)

Detailed Directions by Car:
From Bangor/Caernarfon take the A487 to Porthmadog. From Pwllheli take the A497 to Porthmadog then turn left at the roundabout. From the Midlands take A487 to Portmadog. Once in Porthmadog, follow the brown tourist signs. The line is located right next to Porthmadog Mainline Station, opposite the Queens Hotel.

PUGNEYS LIGHT RAILWAY

Address: Pugneys Country Park, Denby Dale Road, Wakefield WF2 7EQ	**Nº of Steam Locos:** 1
Telephone Nº: 07885 930523	**Nº of Other Locos:** 2
Year Formed: 1998	**Approx Nº of Visitors P.A.:** 16,000
Location of Line:	**Gauge:** 7¼ inches
Length of Line: 1,400 yards	**facebook:** PugneysLightRailway

GENERAL INFORMATION

Nearest Mainline Station: Wakefield (1½ miles)
Nearest Bus Station: Wakefield (2 miles)
Car Parking: Available on site
Coach Parking: Available
Souvenir Shop(s): Yes
Food & Drinks: Available

SPECIAL INFORMATION

Originally an open case mine and gravel quarry, Pugneys Country Park opened in 1985 and has, in addition to the railway, two lakes which cater for sailing enthusiasts.

OPERATING INFORMATION

Opening Times: Weekends and Bank Holidays from April to September (weather permitting) and selected days during the School Holidays. Opening days are weather-dependent during the winter months. Please contact the railway for further information. Open 11.00am to 5.00pm (but until 4.00pm from January to March).
Steam Working:
Visiting locos on rare occasions
Prices: £2.00 per return journey
£1.00 per single journey
Note: Visiting locos are welcome by prior arrangement.

Detailed Directions by Car:
From All Parts: Exit the M1 at Junction 39 and take the A636 towards Wakefield. After approximately ½ mile, turn right at the 2nd roundabout into the Park.

RAINSBROOK VALLEY RAILWAY

Address: Rugby Model Engineering Society, Onley Lane, Rugby CV22 5QD
Telephone Nº: None
Year Formed: 1949
Location of Line: Onley Lane, Rugby
Length of Line: 1,770 yards ground level (7¼ inch) and also 1,100 feet elevated (2½, 3½ & 5 inch gauges)

Nº of Steam Locos: 10
Nº of Other Locos: 4+
Nº of Members: 90
Annual Membership Fee: £45.00
Approx Nº of Visitors P.A.: 6,000
Gauges: 2½ inches, 3½ inches, 5 inches & 7¼ inches
Web site: www.rugbymes.co.uk

GENERAL INFORMATION

Nearest Mainline Station: Rugby (2½ miles)
Nearest Bus Station: Rugby (2½ miles)
Car Parking: Available on site
Coach Parking: None
Souvenir Shop(s): None
Food & Drinks: Light refreshments only

SPECIAL INFORMATION

The Rainsbrook Valley Railway is operated by members of the Rugby Model Engineering Society Ltd.

OPERATING INFORMATION

Opening Times: 2018 dates: 15th April; 20th May; 17th June; 14th & 15th July; 19th August; 16th September, 21st October and 23rd December. Trains run from 2.00pm to 5.00pm (3.00pm to 6.00pm in December).
Steam Working: All operating days
Prices: £1.20 a ride (Under-3s free of charge)

Detailed Directions by Car:
From the M1: Exit at Junction 18 and follow the A428 westwards towards Rugby. After 3 miles turn left on to the B4429 towards Dunchurch. After 1 mile turn left at the crossroads into Onley Lane and the Railway is on the right hand side after 300 yards; From Dunchurch: Follow the A426 Northwards then turn onto the B4429 at the roundabout travelling Eastwards. After 1 mile turn right at the crossroads into Onley Lane for the Railway; From Rugby: In Rugby, follow signs for the Hospital in Barby Road then continue South for 1 mile. At the crossroads go straight on over the B4429 into Onley Lane for the Railway.

READING SOCIETY OF MODEL ENGINEERS

Address: Prospect Park, 59 Bath Road, Reading, Berkshire   RG30 2BJ
Telephone Nº: 07881 960445
Year Formed: 1909 (line since 1975)
Location of Line: Prospect Park, Reading
Length of Line: Two lines, one of 1,100 feet and one of 1,350 feet

Nº of Steam Locos: Approximately 100
Nº of Other Locos: Approximately 20
Nº of Members: 130
Annual Membership Fee: £42.00
Approx Nº of Visitors P.A.: 8,000
Gauge: 2½ inches, 3½ inches, 5 inches and 7¼ inches

GENERAL INFORMATION

Nearest Mainline Station: Reading (2 miles)
Nearest Bus Station: Reading Station (2 miles)
Car Parking: Available on site
Coach Parking: Available by prior arrangement
Souvenir Shop(s): None
Food & Drinks: Available

SPECIAL INFORMATION

The Reading SME has been using the current site for more than 40 years and it now boasts a well equipped club house and useful workshop facilities.

OPERATING INFORMATION

Opening Times: The first Sunday of the month throughout the year and also some Bank Holidays. Please check the web site for further information. Trains run from 1.30pm to 4.30pm (until 4.00pm during the Winter months).
Steam Working: All operating days
Prices: 60p per ride or 10 rides for £5.00

Detailed Directions by Car:
Exit the M4 at Junction 12 and take the A4 Bath Road towards Reading. Continue on this road for approximately 2¼ miles. Prospect Park is on the left, continue along Bath Road almost to the end of Prospect Park and the entrance to the car park for the railway is on the left about 100 metres before the traffic lights.

ROXBOURNE PARK MINIATURE RAILWAY

Address: Roxbourne Park, Field End Road, Eastcote, Ruislip HA4 9PB	**Nº of Steam Locos:** Members locos only
Telephone Nº: None	**Nº of Other Locos:** Members locos only
Year Formed: 1936	**Nº of Members:** Approximately 128
Location of Line: Roxbourne Park	**Approx Nº of Visitors P.A.:** 2,500
Length of Line: 2,200 feet	**Gauge:** 3½ inches, 5 inches & 7¼ inches
	Web site: www.hwsme.org

GENERAL INFORMATION

Nearest Tube Station: Eastcote (½ mile)
Nearest Bus Station: –
Car Parking: Free parking is available on site
Coach Parking: None
Food & Drinks: None

SPECIAL INFORMATION

The railway is operated by members of the Harrow & Wembley Society of Model Engineers which has been running passenger services on the current track in Roxbourne Park since 1979.

OPERATING INFORMATION

Opening Times: 2018 dates: Every Sunday from 25th March to 21st October inclusive with a special Halloween run on 28th October. Trains run from 2.30pm to 5.00pm. Father Christmas trains operate on 9th December. For details of further special events, please check the society's web site.
Steam Working: Every operating day.
Prices: £1.00 per ride

Detailed Directions by Car:
Exit the M40 at Target roundabout and travel into Northolt Village on the A312. Turn left into Eastcote Lane North after the traffic lights just after Northolt Station and continue along this road. Eastcote Lane becomes Field End Road and Roxbourne Park is a little further on opposite Venue '5' (formerly The Clay Pigeon Public House).

ROYDS PARK MINIATURE RAILWAY

Contact Telephone Nº: 0751 802-7702
Year Formed: 1950
Location: Royds Park, Cleckheaton, BD19 5LL
Length of Line: One tenth of a mile

Nº of Steam Locos: 3 (+ members locos)
Nº of Other Locos: 2 (+ members locos)
Nº of Members: 24
Approx Nº of Visitors P.A.: 3,000
Gauge: 3½ inches, 5 inches & 7¼ inches
Web site: www.roydsparkrailway.co.uk

GENERAL INFORMATION

Nearest Mainline Station: Dewsbury (5 miles)
Nearest Bus Station: Cleckheaton
Car Parking: Approximately 20 spaces on site
Coach Parking: None
Food & Drinks: Light refreshments available

SPECIAL INFORMATION

Spenborough Model & Experimental Engineers operate their service on two tracks in Royds Park which are built on the trackbed of the old London & North West Railway. The club operates a Cromar white carriage for wheelchair passengers.

OPERATING INFORMATION

Opening Times: 2018 dates: Every 2nd and 4th Sunday from 25th March to 11th November and also Wednesdays during the summer school holidays. Trains run from 1.00pm to 4.30pm on these dates. Mince Pie Specials run on 9th December from 1.00pm to 4.00pm.
Please check the web site for further information.
Steam Working: Most operating days.
Prices: £1.00 per ride (3 circuits of the track).

Detailed Directions by Car:
Exit the M62 at Junction 26 and turn off at the roundabout onto the A638 Cleckheaton to Dewsbury road. Travel through Cleckheaton for approximately ¾ mile then, just after the start of the dual carriageway, turn left onto New Street and at the top of the street is the entrance to Royds Park.

RYEDALE SOCIETY OF MODEL ENGINEERS

Address: The Old School, Pottergate, Gilling East, North Yorkshire   YO62 4JJ
Telephone No: None
Year Formed: 1983
Location of Line: Gilling East
Length of Line: 450 metres

No of Steam Locos: 10
No of Other Locos: Several
No of Members: 60
Annual Membership Fee: £75.00
Approx No of Visitors P.A.: 3,500
Gauge: 3½ inches, 5 inches and 7¼ inches
Web site: www.rsme.org.uk

GENERAL INFORMATION

Nearest Mainline Station: Thirsk (11 miles)
Nearest Bus Station: Helmsley (5 miles)
Car Parking: Available on site
Coach Parking: Available
Souvenir Shop(s): None
Food & Drinks: Available

OPERATING INFORMATION

Opening Times: 2018 dates: Easter Sunday then every Sunday to 30th September except for 27th May, 10th June and 26th August which are special event days for spectators only (no rides available). Open from 12.30pm to 4.30pm.
Steam Working: Every operating day.
Prices: £1.00 per ride

Detailed Directions by Car:
Gilling East is situated approximately 3 miles south of Helmsley (which is on the A170 Thirsk to Scarborough road). Gilling East is on the B1363 which joins the B1257 at nearby Oswaldkirk. Head West at the crossroads by the Fairfax Arms, signposted for the Golf Club and The Old School is situated on the right after around 200 yards.

SCOTTISH MODEL ENGINEERING TRUST

Address: Wester Pickston Railway, College Road, Glenalmond   PH1 3RX
Telephone Nº: (01764) 653660
Year Formed: 2003
Location: Glenalmond, near Perth
Length of Line: 2,000 metres (2,187 yards)

Nº of Steam Locos: Members' locos only
Nº of Other Locos: Members' locos only
Nº of Members: Approximately 80
Annual Membership Fee: See web site
Approx Nº of Visitors P.A.: 7,500
Gauges: 5 inches and 7¼ inches
Web site: www.smet.org.uk

GENERAL INFORMATION

Nearest Mainline Station: Perth (10 miles)
Nearest Bus Station: Perth (10 miles)
Car Parking: Free parking is available on site
Coach Parking: Available by prior arrangement
Souvenir Shop(s): None
Food & Drinks: Available

SPECIAL INFORMATION

The Trust was formed in 2001 out of the Perth Society of Model and Experimental Engineers which started in 1935. The aim of the Trust is to demonstrate Scotland's engineering heritage through exhibitions, lectures and the sharing of the hobby in general.

OPERATING INFORMATION

Opening Times: 2018 dates: 1st April (Easter Sunday); 27th May; 29th July and 26th August. Open from 11.30am to 4.00pm on these days. In addition, there are always members up at the track every Thursday & Sunday and visitors are welcome.
Steam Working: All open days.
Prices: £2.00 per ride or 6 rides for £10.00

Detailed Directions by Car:
From All Parts: Take the A85 from Perth to Methven and turn right onto College Road opposite the Post Office. The railway is 3 miles to the north of Methven on the right-hand side of the road.

STANSTED PARK LIGHT RAILWAY

Address: Stansted House,
Rowlands Castle   PO9 6DX
Telephone Nº: (023) 9241-3324
Year Formed: 2005
Location: Stansted House, Hampshire
Length of Line: ½ mile
Web site: www.stanstedpark.co.uk/visitor-attractions/stansted-light-railway.html

Nº of Steam Locos: 5
Nº of Other Locos: 3
Approx Nº of Visitors P.A.: 20,000
Gauge: 7¼ inches

GENERAL INFORMATION

Nearest Mainline Station: Rowlands Castle
(1¼ miles)
Nearest Bus Station: Hilsea Portsmouth (5 miles)
Car Parking: Available on site
Coach Parking: Available
Souvenir Shop(s): At the Garden Centre
Food & Drinks: Available

SPECIAL INFORMATION

The railway is located within the grounds of
Stansted House which stands in 1,800 acres of
ancient forest on the South Downs. The line passes
through the Bessborough Arboretum.

OPERATING INFORMATION

Opening Times: Wednesdays, weekends and Bank
Holidays throughout the year and daily during the
School Holidays. Trains run from 11.00am to
4.00pm.
Steam Working: Most opening days during the
Summer, weather permitting.
Prices: Adults £2.00
            Children £1.50 (Free for Under-2s)
            Concessions £1.50

Detailed Directions by Car:
From All Parts: Exit the A3(M) at Junction 2 and take the B2149 towards Rowlands Castle.

STOKE PARK RAILWAY

Address: Burchatts Farm, Stoke Park, Guildford, Surrey GU1 1TU
Telephone Nº: 02392 413324
Year Formed: 1954
Location of Line: Stoke Park, Guildford
Length of Line: 990 feet ground level track and 1,405 feet raised track

Nº of Steam Locos: 6 + visiting locos
Nº of Other Locos: 2
Nº of Members: Over 200
Approx Nº of Visitors P.A.: 10,000
Gauges: 7¼ inches, 5 inches, 3½ inches and 2½ inches
Web site: www.gmes.org.uk

GENERAL INFO

Nearest Mainline Station:
Guildford London Road (½ mile)
Nearest Bus Station:
Guildford (2½ miles)
Car Parking: Street parking + some available on site
Coach Parking:
Street parking only
Souvenir Shop(s): None
Food & Drinks: Available

SPECIAL INFO

The Guildford Model Engineering Society has operated a railway at the Burchatts Farm site since 1958 and two Garden railways also operate on the site.

OPERATING INFO

Opening Times:
2018 Dates: 18th March; 15th April; 20th May; 10th June; 29th July; 19th August; 16th September and 21st October – open from 2.00pm to 5.00pm on these dates. Also open for the Stoke Park Railway Gala weekend on 7th & 8th July from 10.00am to 5.00pm and a Christmas Special operates on 9th December, 11.00am to 3.00pm.
Steam Working: Every open day.
Prices: 1 ride for £1.50
        5 rides for £5.00
Admission prices for the Steam Rally: Adults £8.00
        Under-16s Free of charge
        Senior Citizens £7.00

Detailed Directions by Car:
The Railway is located at the Eastern end of Stoke Park in Guildford, not far from the Spectrum Sports Centre and near to the junction of the A25 (Parkway) and the A3100 (London Road). Access to the Burchatts Farm site is via London Road.

STRAND MINIATURE RAILWAY

Address: Strand Leisure Park, Pier Approach, Gillingham ME7 1TT	**No of Steam Locos**: None
	No of Other Locos: 1
Telephone No: (01634) 333927	**Approx No of Visitors P.A.**: Not known
Year Formed: 1948	**Gauge**: 7¼ inches
Location of Line: Strand Leisure Park	**Length of Line**: 400 yards (circular)
Web site: www.medway.gov.uk/leisurecultureandsport/sportscentres/thestrand.aspx	

GENERAL INFORMATION

Nearest Mainline Station: Gillingham (1 mile)
Nearest Bus Station: Gillingham (1 mile)
Car Parking: Available at the Leisure Park
Coach Parking: None
Souvenir Shop(s): None
Food & Drinks: Cafeteria at the park

SPECIAL INFORMATION

The railway is located within The Strand Leisure Park, one of Medway's most popular leisure attractions.

OPERATING INFORMATION

Opening Times: 2018 dates: Weekends only from 26th May to 22nd July and then daily from 23rd July to 3rd September. Trains run from 11.00am to 5.00pm.
Steam Working: None
Prices: £1.00 a ride (two laps of the track)

Detailed Directions by Car:
Strand Miniature Railway is located within The Strand Leisure Park on the banks of the River Medway in Gillingham. Exit the A2/M2 onto the A289 and follow the road into Gillingham, crossing the bridge over the River Medway into Pier Road. Pass the University of Greenwich Medway campus on the right and continue along Pier Road, passing Liberty Quays before turning left at the roundabout for The Strand.

Strathaven Miniature Railway

Address: George Allan Park, Threestanes Road, Strathaven ML10 6EF
Telephone Nº: (01357) 521995
Year Formed: 1949
Location of Line: George Allan Park
Length of Line: 2,270 feet of 5 inch and 7¼ inch gauge on the ground level track. The raised track of 2½ inch, 3½ inch and 5 inch gauges is 408 feet in length

Nº of Steam Locos: 2 (+ Members locos)
Nº of Other Locos: 3
Nº of Members: Approximately 30
Approx Nº of Visitors P.A.: 12,000
Gauges: 2½ inches, 3½ inches, 5 inches and 7¼ inches
Web: www.strathavenminiaturerailway.org

GENERAL INFORMATION

Nearest Mainline Station: Hamilton (8 miles)
Nearest Bus Station: Hamilton (8 miles)
Car Parking: Available on site
Coach Parking: Available
Souvenir Shop(s): None
Food & Drinks: Available in the Park

SPECIAL INFORMATION

The railway is operated by members of the Strathaven Model Society.

OPERATING INFORMATION

Opening Times: Weekends and Bank Holiday Mondays from Easter until the end of September. Trains run from 1.00pm to 4.30pm.
Steam Working: Most operating days, weather permitting.
Prices: £1.00 per ride

Detailed Directions by Car:
From All Parts: Exit the M74 at Junction 8 and take the A71 through Stonehouse to Strathaven. Turn right onto the A726 and George Allan Park is on the left hand side of the road.

STRAWBERRY LINE MINIATURE RAILWAY

Address: Avon Valley Country Park, Pixash Lane, Keynsham, Bristol BS31 1TF
Telephone Nº: (0117) 986-0124
Year Formed: 1999
Location: Avon Valley Country Park
Web site: www.avonvalleycountrypark.com/train-ride

Nº of Steam Locos: 5
Nº of Other Locos: 30
Approx Nº of Visitors P.A.: 100,000
Gauge: 5 inches
Length of Line: Two-thirds of a mile

GENERAL INFORMATION

Nearest Mainline Station: Keynsham (2 miles)
Nearest Bus Station: Bath (6 miles)
Car Parking: Available on site
Coach Parking: Available
Souvenir Shop(s): Yes
Food & Drinks: Available

SPECIAL INFORMATION

The Strawberry Line operates within the Avon Valley Country Park and is the only commercial railway in the UK which uses a 5 inch gauge.

OPERATING INFORMATION

Opening Times: 2018 dates: Daily, except 25th & 26th December and 1st January. Also closed on Mondays during local school term times. Open from 10.00am to 5.30pm.
Steam Working: Frequently – please contact the railway for further details.
Prices: £1.75 per ride
Note: There is a separate admission charge for entry into the Avon Valley Country Park (cheaper rates apply during off peak times):

> Adults £10.00
> Children £10.50
> Toddlers £4.00 (Under-2s)

Detailed Directions by Car:
From All Parts: Take the A4 from Bath or Bristol to Keynsham and turn into Pixash Lane following the brown tourist signs for the Country Park.

SUMMERFIELDS MINIATURE RAILWAYS

Address: Rook Tree Farm, Cotton End, Bedford   MK45 3BH
Telephone Nº: (01234) 743062
Year Formed: 1948
Location: Off the A600, North of Haynes
Length of Line: Approximately ¾ mile

Nº of Steam Locos: 8
Nº of Other Locos: 7
Nº of Members: Approximately 180
Annual Membership Fee: £32.00
Approx Nº of Visitors P.A.: 10,000
Gauge: 3½ inches, 5 inches & 7¼ inches
Web site: www.bedfordmes.co.uk

GENERAL INFORMATION

Nearest Mainline Station: Bedford (5½ miles)
Nearest Bus Station: Bedford
Car Parking: Available on site
Coach Parking: Available on site
Souvenir Shop(s): None
Food & Drinks: Available

SPECIAL INFORMATION

Summerfields Miniature Railways is operated by the Bedford Model Engineering Society.

OPERATING INFORMATION

Opening Times: 2018 dates: 1st, 2nd, 11th & 22nd April; 6th, 7th, 27th, 28th & 30th May; 10th & 24th June; 8th & 22nd July; 1st, 8th, 15th, 26th & 27th August; 2nd & 16th September; 7th, 21st & 24th October. Santa Specials run on 8th & 9th December (advance booking required for Santa Specials). Trains run from 11.00am to 4.00pm.
Steam Working: On all public running days
Prices: Adult Return £2.00
              Child Return £2.00

Detailed Directions by Car:
From All Parts: The Railway is located by the A600 just to the North of Haynes, 5½ miles South of Bedford and 3½ miles North of Shefford.

SURREY SOCIETY OF MODEL ENGINEERS

Address: Mill Lane, Leatherhead, Surrey, KT22 9AA (No post please as the site does not have a letterbox!) **Telephone Nº:** None **Year Formed:** 1978 **Location of Line:** Mill Lane, Leatherhead **Length of Line:** 2,000 feet	**Nº of Steam Locos:** 10 **Nº of Other Locos:** 8 **Nº of Members:** 48 **Approx Nº of Visitors P.A.:** 15,000 **Gauge:** Both ground and raised level tracks are available covering many gauges **Web site:** www.ssme.co.uk

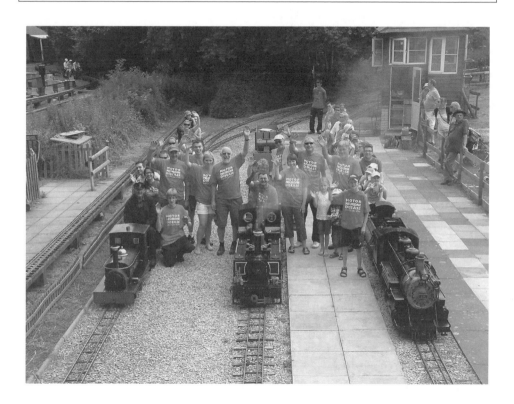

GENERAL INFORMATION

Nearest Mainline Station: Leatherhead (½ mile)
Nearest Bus Station: Leatherhead (½ mile)
Car Parking: Parking on a grass area is possible when conditions allow
Coach Parking: None
Food & Drinks: Available

OPERATING INFORMATION

Opening Times: 2018 dates: 15th April; 7th & 28th May; 24th June; 8th July; 27th August; 9th September and 14th October.
Trains run from 11.00am to 4.00pm. Please contact the railway or check their web site for further details.
Steam Working: All operating days.
Prices: £1.80 per ride
£5.00 multi-ride ticket allows 3 rides
£10.00 multi-ride ticket allows 8 rides

Detailed Directions by Car:
The railway is situated near Leatherhead town centre. Mill Lane is across the road from the well signposted Leisure Centre just off the B2122 Waterway Road and just a short walk to the south of Leatherhead Mainline station.

SWANLEY NEW BARN RAILWAY

Address: Swanley Park, New Barn Road, Swanley BR8 7PW	**Nº of Steam Locos**: 7
Telephone Nº: None	**Nº of Other Locos**: 10
Year Formed: 1986	**Approx Nº of Visitors P.A.**: Not known
Location of Line: Swanley, Kent	**Gauge**: 7¼ inches
Length of Line: 900 yards	**Web site**: steamdriver.wixsite.com/snbr

GENERAL INFORMATION

Nearest Mainline Station: Swanley (¾ mile)
Nearest Bus Station: Swanley (¾ mile)
Car Parking: Available on site
Coach Parking: Available
Souvenir Shop(s): None
Food & Drinks: Available in the Park

SPECIAL INFORMATION

The railway is located in a Swanley Park which also has play areas, paddling pool, sandpit, boating lake, cafeteria, bouncy castle and battery bikes all set in 60 acres of parkland with free access and parking.

OPERATING INFORMATION

Opening Times: 2018 dates: Weekends and most days during the School Holidays from 1st April to 29th September. Trains run from 11.00am to 5.00pm.
Steam Working: Regular steam working but on an ad hoc basis.
Prices: Adult Return £1.50
Child Return £1.00 (Ages 3 to 15)
Family Return £4.00 (2 adults + 2 children)
Note: Lower prices apply for single fares and Under-3s ride for free.

Detailed Directions by Car:
From All Parts: Exit the M25 at Junction 3 and follow green signs for Swanley Park. Go straight on at the first roundabout then turn right at the second roundabout. Continue straight on at the next roundabout then turn left at the next crossroads into New Barn Road. The Park is on the left side of the road.

THAMES DITTON MINIATURE RAILWAY

Address: Willowbank, Claygate Lane, Thames Ditton, Surrey KT7 0LE	**N⁰ of Steam Locos**: 30+
Telephone N⁰: (020) 8398 3985	**N⁰ of Other Locos**: 10+
Year Formed: 1936	**N⁰ of Members**: Approximately 200
Location of Line: Thames Ditton	**Approx N⁰ of Visitors P.A.**: 15,000
Length of Line: ½ mile	**Gauge**: 3½ inches, 5 inches & 7¼ inches
	Web site: www.malden-dsme.co.uk

GENERAL INFORMATION

Nearest Mainline Station: Thames Ditton (½ mile)
Nearest Bus Station: Thames Ditton
Car Parking: Street parking only
Coach Parking: None
Souvenir Shop(s): Yes
Food & Drinks: Available from 2.30pm onwards

SPECIAL INFORMATION

The railway is operated by Malden and District Society of Model Engineers, is well known locally and is referred to as the Thames Ditton Miniature Railway. The Society operates two tracks at the site – a ground level railway is for larger trains and an elevated railway is for the smaller scale trains. Both are used for passenger hauling services.

OPERATING INFORMATION

Opening Times: Open on Easter Sunday and Monday then the first Sunday of each month and every Bank Holiday Sunday and Monday until the first Sunday in November. Trains run from 2.00pm to 5.30pm though the site is open from 1.00pm onwards. Also open during dates in December for pre-booked Santa Specials – please check the web site for further details.
Steam Working: Every operating day.
Prices: Single ride tickets £2.50
        Unlimited ride tickets £7.50
        Family tickets £27.50

Detailed Directions by Car:
Claygate Lane is located just off the A307 Esher to Kingston road about half a mile to the East of the junction between the A307 and A309. If travelling from the East, Claygate Lane is the turning on the left immediately before the railway bridge. If travelling from the West, Claygate Lane is immediately after the second railway bridge though there is unfortunately, no right turn allowed from this direction.

THORNES PARK MINIATURE RAILWAY

Address: Thornes Park, Lawefield Lane, Wakefield WF2 8QZ	**Nº of Steam Locos:** 7
Telephone Nº: (01924) 457690	**Nº of Other Locos:** 4
Year Formed: 1952	**Nº of Members:** 28
Location: Thornes Park, Wakefield	**Annual Membership Fee:** £3.00
Length of Line: ½ mile	**Approx Nº of Visitors P.A.:** 20,000
	Gauges: 7¼ inches

GENERAL INFORMATION

Nearest Mainline Station: Wakefield Westgate (¾ mile)
Nearest Bus Station: Wakefield (1¼ miles)
Car Parking: Available on site
Coach Parking: Available on site
Souvenir Shop(s): None
Food & Drinks: None

SPECIAL INFORMATION

The railway is operated by members of the Wakefield Society of Model and Experimental Engineers. The group is non-profit making and all proceeds after operating costs are donated annually to the Mayor of Wakefield's chosen charity.

OPERATING INFORMATION

Opening Times: Every Sunday (weather permitting) plus Saturdays and Bank Holidays depending on availability of manpower. Trains run from 1.00pm to 5.00pm. Also open for some other special events. Operation is dependent on weather conditions.
Steam Working: Generally whenever the railway is operating.
Prices: Adults 50p
Children 50p (free of charge for infants)

Detailed Directions by Car:
From All Parts: Thornes Park is located approximately 2 miles from Wakefield City Centre, just off the main Huddersfield to Wakefield road (A638).

TONBRIDGE MODEL ENGINEERING SOCIETY

Address: The Slade, Castle Grounds, Tonbridge, Kent TN9 1HR	**N° of Steam Locos**: 40
Telephone N°: 07776 161811	**N° of Other Locos**: 10
Year Formed: 1944	**N° of Members**: Approximately 90
Location: Castle Grounds, Tonbridge	**Approx N° of Visitors P.A.**: 14,000
Length of Line: ¼ mile	**Gauge**: 3½ inches and 5 inches
	Web site: micklow.wix.com/tmes

GENERAL INFORMATION

Nearest Mainline Station: Tonbridge (1 mile)
Nearest Bus Station: Tonbridge (1 mile)
Car Parking: Available on site
Coach Parking: None
Food & Drinks: Available at the swimming pool cafe.

SPECIAL INFORMATION

The Society has run a track at the present site since 1951 and since then facilities have been extended to include a steaming bay and turntable, passenger trollies, refreshment facilities and meeting room, store, and a well appointed workshop.

OPERATING INFORMATION

Opening Times: 2018 dates: Saturday and Sunday afternoons from 1st April to 28th October, weather permitting. Please contact the railway for further information.
Steam Working: Every operating day.
Prices: Free of charge but donations are accepted.

Detailed Directions by Car:
Exit the A21 Tonbridge Bypass at the junction signposted for Tonbridge South. Drive up the High Street, cross over the River Medway and turn left by the sign for the Swimming Pool. Follow the road round, turn left at Slade School and the car park for the railway is directly ahead.

URMSTON MINIATURE RAILWAY

Address: Urmston & District MES Ltd, Abbotsfield Park, Chassen Road, Flixton, Manchester   M41 5DH
Telephone Nº: None
Year Formed: 1948
Location: The Borough of Trafford
Length of Line: 2,200 feet

Nº of Steam Locos: Members' locos only
Nº of Other Locos: Members' locos only
Approx Nº of Visitors P.A.: 5,000+
Gauge: 3½ inches and 5 inches
Web site: www.udmes.co.uk

GENERAL INFORMATION

Nearest Mainline Station: Urmston (1 mile) (Chassen Road Station is closer but no trains stop there on Sundays!)
Nearest Bus Station: Central Manchester (7 miles)
Car Parking: Street parking only
Coach Parking: None
Souvenir Shop(s): None
Food & Drinks: Available from an ice cream van

OPERATING INFORMATION

Opening Times: Sundays throughout the year, except for Christmas Day. Open from approximately 11.00pm to 3.30pm.
Steam Working: Please contact the Society for further information.
Prices: 30p per ride

Detailed Directions by Car:
From the North: Exit the M60 at Junction 10 and take the 3rd exit onto the B2514 heading southwards. Continue straight on at two roundabouts passing the Nag's Head pub into Crofts Bank Road. Shortly after passing the Sainsbury's store, turn right into Flixton Road and pass Urmston station. Continue along Flixton Road then turn left at the roundabout into Chassen Road for the Abbotsfield Park; From the South: Exit the M60 at Junction 9 and turn left onto the B5158 Lostock Road. After approximately ¾ mile, turn left at the roundabout onto Crofts Bank Road (the B2514). Then as above.

VOGRIE PARK MINIATURE RAILWAY

Contact Address: Eskvalley MES,
Roslin Glen Country Park, Roslin,
Midlothian   EH25 9PX
Phone Nº: (01875) 823388 (Secretary)
Year Formed: 1982
Location of Line: Vogrie Country Park
Length of Line: 2000 feet

Nº of Steam Locos: 5 (Member's locos)
Nº of Other Locos: 5
Nº of Members: 30
Approx Nº of Visitors P.A.: 6,000
Gauge: 5 inches and 7¼ inches
Web site: www.eskvalleymes.org.uk
E-mail: vpmr@btinternet.com

GENERAL INFORMATION

Nearest Mainline Station: Edinburgh (9 miles)
Nearest Bus Station: Dalkeith (3 miles)
Car Parking: Available on site
Coach Parking: Available on site
Food & Drinks: Available on site

SPECIAL INFORMATION

The Eskvalley MES operates a railway in the grounds
of the Vogrie Country Park which comprises 105
hectares of woods and Victorian parkland including
a 1876 Victorian mansion (part of which is open to
the public), a nine-hole golf course, adventure
playground and a cafeteria.

OPERATING INFORMATION

Opening Times: Sundays from Easter to September.
Trains run from 2.00pm to 5.00pm.
Steam Working: As available.
Prices: £1.00 per person per ride.
Party bookings can be arranged on other days.
Please phone Geoff on (01875) 823388 or Robin on
07959 856687 for further information.

Detailed Directions by Car:
From Dalkeith: Travel South on the A68 for 2½ miles then turn right onto the B6372 signposted for Vogrie
Country Park. Continue along this road for the Park; From the A7: Travel towards Gorbridge and turn off onto
the B6372. Pass through Gorbridge staying on the B6372, continue through Newlandrig for the Park.

WELLING AND DISTRICT M.E.S.

Address: Falconwood Depot, Eltham Grid Station, off Rochester Way, London, SE9 2RE
Telephone Nº: None
Year Formed: 1945
Location of Line: Adjacent to the UK Power Networks Site, just off Rochester Way
Length of Line: 2000 feet

Nº of Steam Locos: Member's locos only
Nº of Other Locos: Member's locos only
Approx Nº of Visitors P.A.: Not known
Gauge: 3½ inches & 5 inches (raised track)
Web site: www.wdmes.co.uk

GENERAL INFORMATION

Nearest Mainline Station:
Falconwood (¼ mile)
Car Parking: Adjacent to the site
Souvenir Shop: None
Food & Drinks: Hot and cold drinks plus snacks are available

SPECIAL INFORMATION

The railway operates on a site which is owned by UK Power Networks.

OPERATING INFO

Opening Times: 2018 dates:
8th & 22nd April; 6th & 20th May; 3rd & 17th June; 1st, 15th & 29th July; 12th & 26th August; 9th & 23rd September; 7th October. Santa Specials are scheduled to run on 16th December (advance bookings required).
Trains run from 2.00pm to 5.00pm.
Steam Working: All operating days.
Prices: 60p per ride.

Detailed Directions by Car:
The railway is located on the old National Grid site, just off Rochester Way, close to the A2 and near to Falconwood Station. Rochester Way can be accessed directly from the A2 westbound at the Falconwood turn-off. Alternatively, turn off the South Circular at Well Hall Roundabout into Rochester Way, and the railway is then 1¼ miles.

WEST HUNTSPILL M.E.S.

Correspondence: Western Steam, Unit 4A
Love Lane, Burnham-on-Sea   TA9 3QE
Telephone N°: (01278) 788007
Year Formed: 1967
Location: West Huntspill Memorial
Playing Fields, New Road, West Huntspill,
TA9 3QE
Length of Line: 1,100 feet

N° of Steam Locos: Members' locos only
N° of Other Locos: Members' locos only
N° of Members: 65
Approx N° of Visitors P.A.: 8,000
Gauge: 3½ inches & 5 inches (raised track)
Web site: www.westhuntspillmes.co.uk

GENERAL INFORMATION

Nearest Mainline Station: Highbridge (1 mile)
Nearest Bus Station: Highbridge (1 mile)
Car Parking: Available adjacent to the site
Souvenir Shop(s): None
Food & Drinks: None

SPECIAL INFORMATION

Although the West Huntspill Model Engineering
Society was first formed in the early 1950s, the
present site was first used in 1967.

OPERATING INFORMATION

Opening Times: 2018 dates: Every Sunday from
Easter to the end of October, from 2.00pm to
4.30pm. Santa Specials operate on dates in
December from 12.00pm to 4.00pm. Please phone
for further details.
Steam Working: Most operating days.
Prices: £1.00 per ride.

Detailed Directions by Car:
The society's track is located on the West Huntspill Memorial Playing Field. Take the A38 and turn into New Road
by West Huntspill School and the playing fields are on the left after ¼ mile.

WESTON PARK RAILWAY

Address: Weston Park, Weston-under-Lizard, Shifnal, Shropshire TF11 8LE
Telephone Nº: (05601) 132334 (Railway) or (01952) 852100 (Weston Park)
Year Formed: 1980
Location of Line: Weston Park
Length of Line: Approximately 1¼ miles

Nº of Steam Locos: Variable
Nº of Other Locos: Variable
Approx Nº of Visitors P.A.: 19,500
Gauge: 7¼ inches
Web site: www.weston-park.com

GENERAL INFORMATION

Nearest Mainline Station: Shifnal (6 miles)
Nearest Bus Station: –
Car Parking: Available on site
Coach Parking: Available on site
Souvenir Shop(s): –
Food & Drinks: Available

SPECIAL INFORMATION

The railway operates in the grounds of Weston Park (www.weston-park.com), a stately home with a large park and gardens designed by 'Capability' Brown. Weston Park also has a number of other attractions for all the family.

OPERATING INFORMATION

Opening Times: 2018 dates: Daily from 1st April to 15th April, weekends in May then daily from 29th May to 2nd September. Trains run from 11.30am.
Steam Working: Please contact the railway for further details: info@westonrail.co.uk
Prices: Adults £2.50
Children £2.50 (Under-2s ride for free)
Note: Prices shown above are for train fares only. An admission charge is made for entry into the park, gardens and stately home. This admission fee is required for use of the railway. Please contact Weston Park for admission price information.

Detailed Directions by Car:
From All Parts: Weston Park is situated by the side of the A5 in Weston-under-Lizard, Shropshire, just 3 miles from the M54 (exit at Junction 3 and take the A41 northwards) and 8 miles West of the M6 (exit at Junction 12).

WILLEN MINIATURE RAILWAY

Address: South Willen Lake, Milton Keynes MK15 0DS	**Nº of Steam Locos:** None
Telephone Nº: 07810 131737	**Nº of Other Locos:** 1
Year Formed: 1989	**Approx Nº of Visitors P.A.:** More than one million visitors to the Park each year
Location of Line: Milton Keynes	**Gauge:** 7¼ inches
Length of Line: 600 yards	**Web site:** www.willenlake.org.uk

GENERAL INFORMATION

Nearest Mainline Station: Milton Keynes Central (1½ miles)
Nearest Bus Station: Milton Keynes (1½ miles)
Car Parking: Available on site
Coach Parking: Available
Souvenir Shop(s): None
Food & Drinks: Available

OPERATING INFORMATION

Opening Times: Weekends and daily during the summer School Holidays from Easter until the end of October. Open from 11.00am to 5.00pm.
Steam Working: None
Prices: £2.00 per ride

Detailed Directions by Car:
From All Parts: Exit the M1 at Junction 14 and follow the H6 towards Milton Keynes. The lake is to the left of the road by the V10 (Brickhill Street).

WOKING MINIATURE RAILWAY (MIZENS)

Address: Barrs Lane, Knaphill, Woking, Surrey GU21 2JW
Telephone Nº: (020) 8890-1978
E-mail: mizensrailway@rjjagriff.me
Year Formed: 1989
Location of Line: Knaphill, Surrey
Length of Line: 1 mile

Nº of Steam Locos: 10
Nº of Other Locos: 16
Nº of Members: 100
Annual Membership Fee: £15.00
Approx Nº of Visitors P.A.: 20,000
Gauge: 7¼ inches
Web site: www.mizensrailway.co.uk

GENERAL INFORMATION

Nearest Mainline Station: Woking (2½ miles)
Nearest Bus Station: Woking
Car Parking: 175 spaces available on site
Coach Parking: Available on site but advance notification of the visit is necessary.
Souvenir Shop(s): Yes
Food & Drinks: Tea shop open on running days

SPECIAL INFORMATION

The Railway is situated in a beautiful location amidst 9 acres of woodland and takes its name from Mizens Farm which was its original location but is now the headquarters of the McLaren F1 team!

OPERATING INFORMATION

Opening Times: 2018 dates: Easter Sunday then every Sunday from 6th May to 30th September. Also open on Thursdays in August and Santa Specials run on 2nd, 9th & 16th December.
Please check the web site for further details.
Trains operate from 2.00pm to 5.00pm.
Steam Working: Most operating days
Prices: Adult Return From £2.00 or £2.50
Child Return From £2.00 or £2.50
Note: Prices vary depending on the route and Santa Specials must be pre-booked.

Detailed Directions by Car:
From All Parts: Exit the M25 at Junction 11 and follow the A320 to Woking. At the Six Cross Roads Roundabout take the 5th exit towards Knaphill then turn left at the roundabout onto Littlewick Road. Continue along Littlewick Road crossing the roundabout before turning right into Barrs Lane just before Knaphill.

WOLVERHAMPTON & DISTRICT M.E.S.

Address: Baggeridge Country Park, Near Sedgley, Staffordshire	**No of Steam Locos**: 15
Telephone No: (01922) 476373	**No of Other Locos**: 7
Year Formed: 1986	**No of Members**: 60
Location: Baggeridge Country Park	**Approx No of Visitors P.A.**: Not known
Length: Ground level line is being extended to 2,100 feet. Raised track is 420 feet	**Gauge**: 3½ inches, 5 inches & 7¼ inches
	Website: www.wolverhampton-dmes.co.uk

GENERAL INFORMATION

Nearest Mainline Station: Wolverhampton (7 miles)
Nearest Bus Station: Sedgley (2 miles)
Car Parking: Available on site
Coach Parking: Available on site
Food & Drinks: Available

SPECIAL INFORMATION

The Wolverhampton & District Model Engineering Society operates the railway which runs through the Baggeridge Country Park. This was formerly the Baggeridge Colliery and part of the original Himley Estate of the Earls of Dudley. Since the closure of the Colliery, the site has been transformed into 150 acres of attractive country park.

OPERATING INFORMATION

Opening Times: 2018 dates: Public running commences on Easter Sunday, then on all Bank Holidays and most Sundays until mid-September. Detailed information is available on the web site. The railway also operates on Tuesdays and Thursdays during the School Holidays when staff are available. Trains run from 1.00pm to 5.00pm, weather permitting.
Steam Working: Most operating days.
Prices: No charge but donations are accepted.

Detailed Directions by Car:
Take the A449 Wolverhampton to Kidderminster road then turn onto the A463 towards Sedgley. Baggeridge Country Park is just to the South of the A463 after approximately 1 mile and is well-signposted from the road.

WOODSEAVES MINIATURE RAILWAY

Address: Woodseaves Garden Plants, Sydnall Lane Nursery, Woodseaves, Market Drayton   TF9 2AS
Telephone Nº: (01630) 653161
Year Formed: 2004
Location of Line: Shropshire
Length of Line: Over 400 yards

Nº of Steam Locos: 1
Nº of Other Locos: 1
Approx Nº of Visitors P.A.: 1,200
Gauge: 7¼ inches
Web site: www.woodseavesminirail.co.uk
Facebook: Woodseaves Miniature Railway

GENERAL INFORMATION

Nearest Mainline Station: Shrewsbury (19 miles)
Nearest Bus Station: Market Drayton (3 miles)
Car Parking: Available on site
Coach Parking: A small amount of space available
Souvenir Shop(s): None
Food & Drinks: Available in the Tea Shed

SPECIAL INFORMATION

There are two 'Woodseaves' garden centres in close proximity! Specialist Plant Nursery and Gardens Groups are welcome by prior arrangement.

OPERATING INFORMATION

Opening Times: 2018 dates: Sundays and Bank Holidays from Easter to 2nd September, 10.30am to 4.30pm. Also on some Sundays during December. Please contact the railway for further details.
Steam Working: Most operating days
Prices: £1.00 per ride (Under-4s ride for free but must be accompanied by an adult)

Detailed Directions by Car:
From All Parts: The railway is located just off the A529 at Woodseaves, Shropshire which is situated approximately 2 miles to the south of Market Drayton.